. . . *New American Review* meets the reader with a various and engaging personality. It [is] as close to being a representative national literary review as any magazine I know.

—Robie Macauley,
New York Times Book Review

NAR presents a vital dialogue between public concern and private imagination. . . . If *NAR* has a single signature, it is one of complex and aggressive honesty.

—Geoffrey Wolff, *Washington Post*

NAR is a model of open-minded judiciousness . . . clearly an exciting, engaged, vastly well-edited magazine, almost an indispensable one.

—Howard Kaye, *New Republic*

A first-rate blend of good "creative" writing and spacious, skeptical, humane comment, just what all of us are crying out for.

—Frank Kermode, *New York Review of Books*

. . . perhaps the best bargain going in the crowded literary marketplace.

—Saul Maloff, *Newsweek*

if you subscribe
to these views...

NUMBER 15

New American Review

A Touchstone Book
Published by
Simon and Schuster

NEW AMERICAN REVIEW
Editor: Theodore Solotaroff
Managing Editor: Rhoma Paul
Poetry Editor: Richard Howard
Associate Editors: Alice Mayhew, Carol Saltus, W. J. Weatherby
Assistant to the Editor: Debora Sherman

Production Associates: Frank Metz (art), Helen Barrow (design),
Suzanne Frisbie, Tom Kieran, Ruth Randall

Cover design by Roger Hane

A Touchstone Book
Published by Simon and Schuster
Rockefeller Center, 630 Fifth Avenue
New York, New York 10020
New American Review
is published 3 times a year,
in January, April, and August.
Indexed every eighth issue.

FIRST PRINTING

SBN 671–21310–5 Touchstone paperback edition
Library of Congress Catalog Card Number: 67–27377
Manufactured in the United States of America

The editors invite submissions. Manuscripts will
not be returned unless accompanied
by stamped self-addressed envelope.

Contents

Editors' Notes

BRIAN MOORE's long story, "Catholics," is about the continuing agonies of organized religion. The rebels have taken over the organization, only to impose equally rigid forms and to press for an authoritarian control of their own. Once more, it is the power structure that defines heresy in a Church more concerned with authority than with faith. From this angle, "Catholics" is in the tradition of those political novels and stories that deal with Big Brotherism—the corruption of revolutionary movements into new tyrannies, the stamping out of dissidence and individuality, and thereby, dissidents and individuals.

When a civil institution attempts to impose its single will, it steps outside the bonds of the just social contract, no matter what its ends or motives may be, or what it hopes to gain for some members of the society. When a religious institution univocally defines and limits the relation between God and man, it meddles in one of the deepest mysteries of the human soul. In making itself more than mediator, larger than its community, and prouder than humanity, it is in danger of making itself an idolatrous god. It breaks the First Commandment, I am the Lord thy God, thou shall not have false gods before Me. Failing in love and denying its humanity, such a Church wanders from the two commandments Jesus told us contain all the others: Thou shall love God, and Thou shall love thy neighbor.

Moore's story is set toward the end of the Twentieth Century. The *Fourth* Vatican Council has taken place, and a new world order of Judeo-Christian churches has been established (apparently under the initiative of the Roman Church), which is seemingly broader in its bases of belief, but as narrow in its disciplines as the Roman Church had been some thirty-five years ago. Not surprisingly, there is rebellion, and this story, in dealing with one small revolt by some Irish monks, tells us a great deal about the nature and marks of faith. It tells us that faith can not be legislated, or commanded, as one elderly monk complains; and that one man's faith may not be visible to another. Interestingly enough, in this new age of ecumenism, with all the Western churches united dogmatically, there is a grander unanimity than before, nowhere to escape to except into open revolt or new heresies.

Moore sets before us the stubborn question of whether religion is essentially a set of rules, a canon, or whether it is a community of prayer. Is the Church an organization founded on obedience to doctrines that may even contradict each other from era to era, or is the Church, as John XXIII said way back in 1962 at the beginning of the Second Vatican Council, "the people of God"?

If John is correct, then the Church must be organic. It is a community of striving. There are many persons in the community (as Jacques Maritain reminded us so long ago) and they are not merely numbers. The Abbot and his monks, in Brian Moore's story, and the protagonist in Anne Higgins' "In Search of a Missing IUD" are both caught in the disciplinary web of a Church that seems not to regard them as full persons. In the Higgins story, a Jewish-Catholic convert is the victim of the narrow reading of the Natural Law on "artificial" birth control, threatened in her personhood, burdened with babies beyond her endurance, and driven to despair by an institution that puts its own demands for order and consistency before the deeper needs and wants of the believing community. By Moore's future era, the matter would have been long since dismissed, and with it a certain set of assumptions. But are things so very different in his Church? How goes it with the people?

In "Catholics" two more Councils have met and debated and ordered and proscribed. Ecumenism has been accomplished among the Western Churches, and they have made a political commitment to negotiate an opening with the
(Continued on page 231)

Catholics

A NOVELLA

Brian Moore

1

THE FOG LIFTED. The island was there. The visitor
walked to the end of the disused pier and saw it across
three miles of ocean, riding the sea like an overturned fishing boat. Morning sunlight moved along a keel of mountain, above valleys black as tarred boatsides.

He thought of Rome. Surprisingly, the Order itself had
little descriptive information. In the Lungotevere Vaticano
he had been handed an out-of-print book: *Weir's Guide to
Religious Monuments.*

MUCK ABBEY, Kerry, Ireland. On a small island off the
rocky panoramic coastline of the Atlantic ocean known
as "The ring of Kerry." The Monastery (Albanesian
Order), founded 1216, rebuilt 1400–70, has a depend-
ency, or cell, on the mainland, the priory of Holy Cross,
at Mount Coom, near the village of Cahirciveen. This
priory, sacked by Cromwellian troops, was, in Penal
times, a site for clandestine Mass, conducted in the open
air on a "Mass rock" altar. The Abbey itself (on Muck
Island) escaped Cromwellian despoliation and sits on
the western slope of the island overlooking a splendour
of sea. From the Abbey tower the visitor looks down on
grey waves which curl on barren rock. The monks fish
and gather kelp.

He had telephoned again before breakfast. The pretty girl at the desk in his hotel cranked up an incredibly old-fashioned device to call Exchange. "We're wanting Muck Island. No, Sheilagh, it's all right, it's for that priest who spoke to the island last night."

"There now, Father." He took the receiver. A bell rang and rang.

"Muck Island One," said a crackly voice, out in the Atlantic.

The visitor gave his name. He said he had been asked to call and check on the weather.

"What was your name again, now?"

"Kinsella. *Father* James Kinsella." He had learned his lesson.

"Ah, Father Kinsella. We'll send a boat for you, to be sure. Go you down to the pier now, and Padraig will be along shortly."

Gulls, searching the remains of fish, skimmed overhead, dipped to the brackish waters beneath. Behind him, at the end of the road which led to the pier, were three roofless concrete boat sheds, floored with weeds, smelling of urine and sheep droppings. A very old car, which he had thought abandoned, sat in one of the sheds. Yesterday, when he first drove down here searching the fog for a sight of the island, he had looked in at the car. A purple silk stole lay on the front seat. At the hotel, after dinner, he asked who had built this pier. No, the monks had not built it, the Irish Government built it, years ago, before the fishing became polluted. At that time, there were some twenty families living on the island. "They've nearly all come out since. Scattered now, to the four ends of the world."

"Polluted. Does that mean the monks don't fish any more?"

"Ah, no, the fishing is grand again. The water was cleaned up, a while back. The trouble is, it was done too late for the people of Muck. There do be only four families left on the island. And the monks."

The old car he had seen in the boat shed, was it the monastery car?

"It is, indeed. The monks do use it to drive to Cahir-civeen of a Sunday. It's twenty miles, Father."

"But, what if the sea is rough, or if there's a fog, and a boat can't come over from the island?"

"Then no Mass is said at Cahirciveen."

No Mass? Yesterday's sights filled his mind; the streets of this Kerry village, gray nineteenth-century façades, market square, gray Gothic church, streets built before, and impassable to, today's traffic. Now existing in permanent confusion, cars, buses, trucks, campers, vans, moving in an endless clogged procession in and out of the narrow streets while, on the outskirts, more vehicles were bogged in the muddy confusion of improvised car parks and tent villages. And everywhere in Cahirciveen, jammed into the shops and pubs, herded into the main square like beasts on a fair day, the pilgrims. No one knew how many they were on any given weekend, but for months there had not been a room or a bed to rent for fifty miles around. They were Irish, of course, but there seemed an almost equal number from England and Scotland. Others came by car ferry and charter plane from the Continent; an emphasis of French, but also many Germans and even some pilgrims from Rome itself. The Americans had flown in two charter groups, many of them old souls who had never crossed the Atlantic before. They came, it seemed, simply to hear at least one Mass, say the rosary, and leave. The uncomfortable local accommodations did not encourage a long stay. It was a phenomenon, even in the history of pilgrimage. There were no miracles, there was no hysteria, there was not even a special fervor. The mood was nostalgic. The pilgrims rose early on Sunday morning, went in buses and cars to the foot of Mount Coom, five miles from the village. There, they ascended the mountain, on foot, to kneel on muddied grassy slopes, or on shelves of rock, often in the unyielding Irish rain. Most could see the Mass rock and the priest only from a distance, but all heard the Latin, thundering from loudspeakers rigged up by the townsfolk. Latin. The communion bell. Monks as altarboys saying the Latin responses. Incense. The old way.

"No Mass?" he said to the hotelkeeper. "But when they've come all this way, what do they do if there's no Mass?"

"Ah, now, Father, that's a grand thing to see. The pilgrims just stay there, kneeling and saying the rosary. They stay all day, waiting and praying."

"But don't some of them try to go out to the island itself?"

The hotelkeeper laughed, showing gap teeth. "No fear! No boat can land on Muck that doesn't know the trick of it. And the island boats will land nobody without the Abbot's permission. Besides," the hotelkeeper said, serious again. "These pilgrims do be good people. When the Abbot put up a sign in the church here in Cahirciveen saying 'Parishioners Only For Confession,' most of the pilgrims stopped bothering the monks. Mind you, the lines are still long. After Mass, on a Sunday, there do be three monks, hard at it in the church until it's time for them to take the boat back."

"But why do the confessions take so long?"

"We still have private confessions. One person at a time in the box."

Private confessions. *This* was not known in Rome. "What about public confessions?"

"Public confessions, Father?"

"Where the whole congregation stands before Mass and says an act of contrition?"

"Ah, that never took here."

Anger, sudden and cold, made Kinsella say: "It took everywhere else!" Ashamed, he saw the hotelkeeper bob his head, obedient, rebuked but unconvinced.

YESTERDAY WHEN he first arrived by car from Shannon Kinsella had carried a paramilitary dispatch case, a musette bag, and was wearing gray-green denim fatigues. At the desk of Hern's Hotel, the girl was curt. The hotel was full, there was a two-month waiting list, no reservations had been made for days. "But you took my reservation," he said. "You confirmed it, and the confirmation was telexed from Dublin to Amsterdam Ecumenical Center. This *is* Hern's Hotel, isn't it?"

"What was your name again, sir?"

"James Kinsella. Catholic priest," he said, in the ecumenical manner.

"Oh, Father Kinsella. Oh, excuse me, Father. We have a room for you, certainly."

Father. In the crowded hotel lobby, every available seat was occupied. Standees circled disconsolately around racks of seaside postcards and shelves of paperback books. *Father.* Sun-reddened faces turned to stare, supercilious of his American accent, his ecumenical clothes. Most of these pilgrims were older than he, old enough to remember the Latin Mass. But there were young ones too, former Catholic Pentecostals, now eager for experience as the *penitentes* of the day. Their scorn toward him, his own scorn in reverse, met him as he went toward the stairs and the privileged bedroom. His friend Visher, a behaviorist, had made a study of current Catholic attitudes toward their clergy. "People are sheep," Visher said. "They haven't changed. They want those old parish priests and those old family doctors. Sheep need authoritarian sheepdogs nipping at their heels from birth to funeral. People don't want truth or social justice, they don't want this ecumenical tolerance. They want certainties. The old parish priest promised that. You can't, Jim."

WAVES LAPPED the slimed boat steps. A new sound entered Kinsella's ear, the pulse of an engine. He looked at the sea but saw no boat. Sound, preceding vision, carrying clear over the whitecapped waves. Pulsing. Coming, coming; the painful confrontation. He and the Abbot of Muck.

"THIS WILL NOT BE your first visit to Ireland," Father General said, looking up from the file. It was a statement, not a question, but he felt he should answer it.

"No, sir. In my last year at Harvard, I went over there to attend a summer school. The Yeats school, in Sligo. My ancestors were Irish. They came from County Mayo, I believe. It's in the West, where this abbey is."

"William Butler Yeats." The General smiled his faint, Prussian smile. " 'What rough beast, its hour come round at last.' Appropriate. I want you to bury this beast. And I think the way to do that is for me to give you plenipotentiary status. Emissaries who must report back to headquarters, especially young ones, would seem to these old mastodons to be mere novices. I will make clear to this abbot that you are me. What you decide will be the Order's final edict."

"What about the Father Provincial in Dublin, sir?"

The General sighed. "It seems that he and the Abbot of Muck have a disagreement going back as far as the Pauline papacy. As you know, since Vatican IV, bishops are no longer bound by the orders of provincials. These Irish abbots are mitered and of episcopal rank. Each is a prelatus nullius, belonging to no one. This one has chosen to ignore the provincial's recommendations. However, he cannot ignore mine." Father General picked up a Xerox sheet, a facsimile of an old chapter-house record book, microfilmed, its original now destroyed. "The recalcitrant Abbot of Muck," the General said. "Let's see. He is one Tomás O'Malley, now in his sixty-ninth year, the son of a greengrocer. What is a greengrocer, I wonder?"

"A seller of vegetables, sir."

"Ah. The Abbot is the product of an Irish seminary, a place called Kilcoole. Prizewinner, Latin, oh, lala! Doctorate in—can't read this script, must be uncial—doesn't matter. Four years at Buckmore Abbey in Kent. Then, Ireland, Dublin, hmm, hmm, and appointed Abbot of Muck. Cast down on some remote little island and abandoned at a relatively early age, it would seem the Order had no great hopes of him. Subsequent life of poverty, thirty monks, fishermen all, income from kelp and dulse, whatever that is, and manure sales—well, that's quite enough of that. You can look this over at your leisure." The General picked up an Order Fact Form. "Now, this gives the age of the Abbey, details of grants, et cetera. I think I see why the media people are interested, sick as we all are nowadays for a past we never knew. The monastery was founded in twelve-sixteen." The General lolled in his Eames chair and looked out of the tall windows of his office. Below was the new pedestrian mall of the Lungotevere Vaticano and, beyond it, the dull, muddy flow of the Tiber. The General's eye moved left to fix on the roofs of the Vatican, and the dome of St. Peter's, immense, even at a distance. "The year twelve hundred and sixteen. Think of it. The fourth Lateran council had just closed. Innocent the Third was in the chair of Peter. And that great monstrosity down the road there was three hundred years away from being built."

He looked again at the Fact Form. "In the beginning the Abbey was not ours. It was founded by some local king, at the behest of Patrick, an Irish bishop saint. The Albanesians petitioned to take over in fourteen-oh-six. Within a couple of hundred years they owned half the lands of Kerry, which is why they have this priory on the mainland. The Abbot of Muck has always had the right to appoint the prior of the cell of Holy Cross at Cahirciveen."

"I believe there is no prior there now, sir."

"That's right, yes." The General consulted the Fact Form. "There are nearby parishes, of course, but the monks still cross to the mainland to say Mass and perform sacerdotal duties. And the changes that have taken place elsewhere in our time have simply been bypassed at Cahirciveen. Our Irish provincial has made 'suggestions' on four differing occasions, but this abbot remains blind and dumb. I wonder how long it would have gone on, if it had not been for the tourists? Anyway, it was a B.B.C. crew which did the damage. Latin Mass. Imagine that," the General said, and smiled. "I'd rather like to see one again, wouldn't you?"

"I don't really remember it, sir."

"Backs to the congregation, vestments, *introibo ad altare dei*. And the bell! The Sanctus! Oh, lala, how one forgets. And now it's packing them in. Listen to this. Ferry tours from Liverpool and Fishguard, charter flights from Leeds, Boston, New York—pilgrimage from France—even *bella Italia*." The General's amusement turned to a fit of sneezing. He used a nasal inhaler, then stared again at the brownish waters of the Tiber. "It is cliché to say it was to be expected. Even Vatican IV can't bury two thousand years in a few decades. But, I'd have thought Spain. Or, perhaps, some former Portuguese possession." The General sighed. "We are so infallibly fallible, aren't we? Wasn't it Chesterton who said something about a thing too big to be seen? Ireland. Of course! Well, here you are. Take the file. Let my secretary have your itinerary. I'd suggest you hop a supersonic tonight and go straight to Amsterdam. It's a formality, of course, but in an affair of this kind everything should be strictly kosher." He smiled. "I'll alert the council that you are my plenipotentiary. After Amsterdam, get straight over to Ireland. Remember, I want this settled by the end of the month."

"Yes, sir."

"Get that old fool down off that mountain, James. And if he gives you any trouble—bite him!"

A FISHING BOAT was instantly in sight, bashing through the tops of the whitecaps, as though in the moment Kinsella had looked away some Brobdingnagian hand had painted it into the seascape. A diesel-engined ten-tonner, it was built to scramble up and over these gray walls of waves. The wind force increased, sending a great slap of water over the edge of the pier. A black storm cloud filled the edge of the horizon. As the fishing boat approached across the strait, Kinsella picked up his dispatch case which contained the General's letter and an Order Plenipotentiary, signed in Amsterdam by the four current members of the World Ecumen Council. He walked to the stone steps as the boat cut its engines and drifted outside the bar. A man in a tweed hat appeared and moved about in the bow. Another stood in the wheelhouse, a stout young fellow in a white turtleneck sweater. Not monks, as he had expected, but islanders, the few fisher families still living on the Abbot's domain. The man in the tweed hat untied a black curragh, which floated light as a mussel shell at the stern of the ten-tonner. Pulling it close, he jumped in, raised long oars, and rowed strongly toward the pier, the curragh swinging up like an amusement park gondola to hang on the whitetipped peaks, then fall, dizzyingly, into the trough of waves. The mother boat heeled. With a rattle, an anchor spilled like entrails from its bow, falling deep into the sea. The stout youth came out of the wheelhouse and stood at the side, staring across the water at Kinsella. With his curling red hair, freckled skin, snub nose, and white fisherman's sweater he looked like Dylan Thomas.

The curragh, stroked easily now that it had passed into

the shelter of the pier, came toward the steps where Kinsella waited. The rower had his back to the steps. Skillful, he shipped the oars as he glided alongside, his hand, with the blind touch of practice, finding the solitary iron bollard at the foot of the steps.

As the tweed-hatted rower turned to look back at the pier, a smile rose on Kinsella's face, an American smile, the currency of greeting. But the rower's eyes moved past him as though he were some idle seabird come to rest on the pier. Eyes swept the pier, the sheds, the road beyond, then, reluctantly, came back to him. "Morning," the boat-man said.

"Hello, there." Kinsella, smiling, moved confidently down the last slimed steps toward the curragh. But the boatman shook his head, warning him not to board. The boatman was young, vulpine, with a wild cub's grace. His gray eyes stared, as the eyes of an animal stare from a zoo cage.

"I'm James Kinsella, Catholic priest," Kinsella said, from Ecumenical habit.

The boatman's tongue appeared, round as a teat be-tween his teeth. Its owner sucked on it, staring, silent.

"*Father* Kinsella," Kinsella corrected himself.

"Ah, come off it," the boatman said, in a soft island brogue.

"I'm sorry?"

"I come for a priest. I can't take nobody else. Sorry, now."

"But I'm the man you came for. I *am* a priest."

The boatman, sucking his tongue again, looked past Kinsella, again searching the pier, the sheds, the road beyond. Then turned to look out at the fishing boat anchored at the bar. On deck, Dylan Thomas raised his head in query.

"Not here yit," the boatman called.

The boy on deck turned and looked back at the distant mass of the island. The fat black cloud was now immense, moving like a dark lens across the sky. The boatman also stared up at the sky.

"Storm coming up?" Kinsella asked.

" 'Tis."

"Well, let's go, then. Do you want to see my papers, or something?"

"Come off it," the boatman said, again. He turned away as though Kinsella had already disappeared. Sat in the long, light curragh, gripping the bollard, steadying the craft which bobbed on the lapping pier waves. Sucked his round tongue for a moment, then yelled across the water. "There's no-o ca——aaaa-ar!"

On deck the white-sweatered boy pointed to the sky. "Let's go—o b—aack, Padraig," he called, syllables of sound separated in their transit across the waves.

The boatman abruptly let go of the bollard and took up his oars. Kinsella, irritated, reached down and caught hold of the curragh's stern.

"Let go of that."

"I tell you, I am Father Kinsella. The Abbot is expecting me."

Padraig, the boatman, let go of one oar, seized up a steel rowlock from beneath it and, swift as a biting dog, struck the knuckles which held the curragh's stern. With a gasp of pain, Kinsella drew his hand back. The rowlock snapped into its hole, the oar in it, and, with two swift strokes, the boatman swung the curragh out of reach.

"YOU DON'T LOOK like a priest, I just can't imagine you as one." His mother said that, long ago, when in his second year at college he decided to study with Hartmann. Agnostic herself, his mother had continued her son's religious education after her Catholic husband died. She was one for keeping promises. Futures were another matter, as her son found when he told her he intended to become a Catholic priest. Useless to instance that his new hero, Gustav Hartmann, had taken Holy Orders as an Albanesian monk, much as Malraux had become a Minister of State in the Fifth Republic, not for the obvious condition, but as a means toward social action. Which, in Hartmann's case, had made him a twentieth-century Bolívar to this generation of South American revolutionary priests and nuns. The Church, Hartmann taught, despite its history and its dependence on myth and miracle, exists today as the quintessential structure through which social revolution can be brought to certain areas of the globe. But Kinsella's mother, a Liberal, born in the nineteen thirties, did not believe in the combination of Holy Orders and revolutionary theory. She, like that fisherman rowing away from him now, could not see things as they really were.

THE CURRAGH tied up beside the fishing boat. The fishing boat's engine came to life, the anchor growled up from the sea. As the fishing boat, turning, churning, headed back toward open waters, Kinsella found himself running up the pier toward his rented car. Jumped in, went breakneck toward Cahirciveen and a telephone. He was a priest and they had not known he was a priest because the priests they knew wore black suits, or the clothes of old women, long brown habits, sandals, thick belts knotted about with big rosary beads, and he must telephone and order them to turn that boat around and send it back for him at once.

Four miles from the pier, driving through the flat trench landscape of a turf bog, he came, unexpectedly, to a crossroads. A whitewashed cottage stood on one corner, and what seemed to be a larger cottage, also whitewashed, but with a big barn behind it, faced on the opposite corner. On the doorway of the larger cottage was a sign.

P. MCGINN: LICENSED TO SELL WINES & SPIRITS

And a smaller sign, in Gaelic: TELEFON.

Hens rose in fright as he swerved into the cobbled yard. A rooster ran past, wattles loose, one skelly eye fixed on the car in wild alarm. Inside the pub it was dark as evening. Two Irish laborers, wearing greasy old black suits, once their Sunday best, now their daily dungarees, white shirts open at the neck, and knee-length rubber Wellington boots. Faces the color of strawberry jam looked up from large glasses of black porter. Behind the small bar, a man, broad as a rainbarrel, wearing a white turtle-neck sweater, wiped glasses with a linen cloth. "G'day," said he, to Kinsella. " 'Twill rain, I would say."

"I want to telephone Muck Island."

"You wouldn't get them."

"I'm a priest. They're expecting me."

Strawberry faces of the laborers bobbed uniformly in greeting, as though Kinsella had just entered the pub. "G'day, Father," in unison, they sang. From beneath the bar the proprietor took up a receiver on a hand-crank stand, cranked it up, spoke in a language which Kinsella assumed to be Gaelic. Then: "There, Father. There you are, so."

The crackly island voice, "What? What? . . . Padraig didn't get you? Ah, sure that's a disaster." And, over the wire, wheezing laughter. "Didn't know you were a priest? Oh, God love us! I'm sorry, Father, but do you see that weather out there, I'm afraid we'll not get you in today . . . What? What?"

He had to shout. Three faces watched him in that small, hop-stinking room. "Send the boat back! I have to get there today. It's urgent."

"Well, now, Father, the minute the wea– th– er clears, do you heeeee– do you heeeee–aaa-arr?"

Static crackles. Silence. Then a girl's voice. "You were cut off, Father. It's a bad connection at the best of times. I could try them later, if you like?"

"I'll call you," he said, and put the phone down.

Three faces turned to him. Unlike people from more civilized places they did not pretend that they had not overheard. Strawberry cheeks bunched in grins. "So, Padraig refused you," the proprietor said. "Isn't that a good one!"

They laughed. It was.

"Those boys on the island, you see," the proprietor explained. "They never come out, they have no notion that the priests out here do be just like the rest of us, nowadays. Begging your pardon, Father. Are you an American?"

"Yes."

"A grand country, so. You'll get out tomorrow. I'd say 'twill clear."

" 'Twill clear," one of the laborers promised.

"How much do I owe you for the phone?"

"Ah, not at all."

"Well, thank you. Thank you very much."

"G'day, Father."

"G'day, Father."

"Thank you again," Kinsella said.

Outside, in the cobbled yard, hens tacked cautiously around his feet. He looked at the crossroads and there, blurring its outlines, was a rainbow's end. The rainbow arched up and away from this place to disappear behind a brow of mountain. Raindrops spat warnings. Hens stalked to cover. Rain came, wetting to a thick flow. As Kinsella retreated into the shelter of the pub doorway, thunder banged above him. Thunderclouds, massing over the far mountain, advanced to take possession of the sky.

He felt cold. He thought of Hartmann in the rain forests of Brazil. He looked again for the rainbow, but it had vanished, shimmering, in that sudden rain. It had appeared, then disappeared, in this lonely place, a place which now, in its noon darkness, made him think of a Beckett landscape, that place in which Vladimir and Estragon might have waited for Godot. The rainbow had seemed to end, down there, in the center of the white cross formed by two concrete ribbons of road. In such phenomena people once read signs of God's hand. He turned and went back into the pub.

2

THE HELICOPTER drifted over the crossroads, the pub, the yard, then, tilting slightly forward, moved downwind to land in a field on the edge of the bog. The rotor blades still turned at take-off speed as Kinsella hurried toward the machine in the afternoon's continuing drizzle, ducking under the great propellers as the pilot slid the door aside and held out a hand to take him up. He sat, buckling his seat belt. The door shut. The green and white helicopter, the wind from its rotor blades flattening the whin bushes of the field, rose like some huge dragonfly, its legs, which had bent on hinges under it, stiffening and retracting as it rose in flight. It poised, then tilting forward, moved up and out. Away.

Below, three faces mooned up, the laborers and the publican. Like children they waved as the helicopter lurched over them. And were gone. Kinsella looked at the pilot, a young man of his own age, dark-haired and smiling, staring ahead into the fog and rain. The pilot wore a uniform of black coveralls, but with showy encrustations of gold braid at wrists and shoulders, and, on the peak of his cap, a gold crest. Caparisoned like some admiral of former days, he seemed a personage of importance. Kinsella reflected on the times; cardinals went shabby in mufti, hirelings of all kinds had increased their false panoply of rank.

"Have you ever been on the island?" he shouted at the pilot.

"No, but I've flown over it."

Thunder. Lightning sheeted the sky. Within three minutes, they were over the ocean, a rough sea pitted by rain squalls, but ahead, toward the west, a shaft of sunlight like a stage flood. The pilot pointed to it, grinning and winking to show this was good news. Kinsella nodded. He had waited three hours for the helicopter, fretting, worrying that it would not find the lonely crossroads. In action once more, airborne, traveling at speed, his confidence returned. He would be diplomatic, but firm. With luck, he could have agreement before nightfall.

Now they were over the island, chopping along above a deserted strand, fine gray sand, green grassy dunes, and, at the edge of the sweep of beach, a harbor with a stone pier and two fishing boats tied up at it. One was the ten-tonner which had refused him that morning. Beyond the pier was a ruined medieval castle, built strategically on a green headland, commanding the sea approach. He pointed at it and the pilot, nodding, flew up and hovered the helicopter over the roofless castle maw.

"The fort of Granuaile," the pilot shouted.

"What?"

"Very old. Grace O'Malley built it and lived in it."

"Who?"

"Grace O'Malley. The Sea Queen. Granuaile."

Circling the headland, the helicopter moved down the spine of the island, flying over the village adjoining the fort. The village was a street of a dozen whitewashed cottages, with hen-littered backyards in which were rough

stone sheds housing animals and tools. As Kinsella peered
down, two small children ran out, stared, then waved. Four
of the dozen houses in the street were abandoned, windows
broken, holes in the roofs. The helicopter bucked into
stormy wind, lurched up and away over tiny fields divided
into jagged squares by walls of roughly piled boulders. A
road, never paved, led off to two other farms, long abandoned. The helicopter, using the road as marker, curved
across the bay, climbed a hillside to a mountain pass,
dipped into the pass, was surrounded by walls of gray
Gothic rocks, then came out to beauty, on the western
slope of the island, to the Abbey, as the old guidebook
had said, on a headland, *a splendour of sea. From the
Abbey tower, the visitor looks down on grey waves which
curl on barren rock.* The helicopter, strange dragonfly,
wheeled and went down on a field to the left of the
monastery, rotor blades fanning the grasses, as it came to
rest, its strange legs extending, bending to accommodate
its weight as it touched ground. The plexiglass door slid
open. The rotor blades became visible, whirling, slowing.

"Was it to be the blackberries in the glass jars and the
redcurrants in the stone pots? Or was it the other way
around, you told me?"

Brother Paul, filled with the demanding urgency which
infects the deliberations of small minds, entered the
Abbot's parlor, above the chancery of the Abbey, without
knock or by-your-leave. The Abbot, looking out through
the narrow aperture of a thirteenth-century window, did not
answer at once. When he did, he said, "Blackberries. Jars."

"Ah, I was right, so I was. I thought it was the blackberries in the glass jars. Would you come down yourself
now, and have a look at the fruit?"

"We have a visitor," the Abbot said.

"A visitor?" Brother Paul was alarmed. "Ah, no. Sure,
didn't Padraig go out this morning and come back empty?
And no other boat could come in, in this weather."

But the Abbot did not seem to hear. "His vorpal blade
went snicker-snack," the Abbot said. "It would be a
good description of that helicopter out there."

"A what?" Brother Paul bustled to the window. "Oh,

that's that yoke from Dingle. I've seen it many's the time passing over here. Is he broke down, or what? Why did he land?"

The Abbot looked at Paul. "Did you not hear it come over, a minute ago?"

Paul blushed. He was deaf, ashamed of it, and a bad liar. "How would I hear it and I down in the calefactory room taking the stems off berries?"

"Go on back down, now," the Abbot said, suddenly weary of Paul. "I had better see to our visitor."

But Paul lingered, his head close to the Abbot's in the vise of the narrow medieval window. "That's not the priest from Rome, surely?"

"I would say it is."

"They'd have to wear special clothes to go up in one of them things," Brother Paul announced. He had not traveled to the mainland in a decade, and had never traveled by air.

"Yes." The Abbot turned from the window. "Go along now and tell Brother Martin to bring the visitor up directly. There is no sense in my climbing the stairs twice."

"I will do that, then," Brother Paul said.

The Abbot turned back to the window. The green and white helicopter increased its engine noise, the blades blurring to invisibility. *The frumious bandersnatch,* the Abbot said to himself. The words fuming and furious made frumious, and frumious it was now as it rose, levitating a few feet above the grass, hesitating as though looking for directions. Getting its bearings, it tilted forward, moving up and out to sea. He will stay the night, the Abbot decided. I will ask Father Manus to get us salmon from the pool. The sky was clearing, but, out there toward Slea Head, the wind force was building. There would be rain.

He heard steps, uncertain, coming up the winding stone staircase beneath his parlor, heard, predictably, Martin's warning. "The ninth step is longer than the others, Father. The trip step, they called it in the old days. Be careful, so."

"Thank you," said the visitor in his American voice, the voice the Abbot had heard on the telephone. Footsteps reached the top of the second flight. Good. It would not do to trip Rome up. "This way, Father," the Abbot called.

To Kinsella, turning and turning in that cold stone turret, to come out through the narrow door into the Abbot's parlor was dizzying, confusing, causing him, at first, to miss his host's welcoming hand.

"How are you, Father." The Abbot's voice was very soft.

"I'm sorry, excuse me, how are you. Good to meet you, Father Abbot."

"So Padraig left you standing on the pier. Oh, he's thick, that lad. I am sorry you had a such a lot of trouble."

"It wasn't his fault. He didn't realize I was a priest."

"But you came on, anyway. Enterprising. Do you know, Father, that's the first flying machine of any description that has ever landed on Muck? You've brought us the symbol of the century. Just when I thought we'd be able to close the hundred years out, and say we missed our time."

"Would you have preferred that, Father Abbot?"

"Preferred what?"

"To have missed this century, to have been born in another time?"

"I should think not," the Abbot said. "If we had lived in the eighteenth century, for instance, our religion was under interdiction by the English. And the nineteenth century was not much better. Unless you had a lust for becoming a martyr, the past was not a time to be a Catholic priest here."

"Yes, of course. I forgot," Kinsella said. "By the way, I have a letter for you from Father General. And this is my Ecumenical Order of Mission. Perhaps you'd care to to have a look at them?"

The Abbot would indeed. He stretched out his hand. "An Irish name, you have," he said, as Kinsella undid his dispatch case.

"Yes."

"That is a County Mayo name." The Abbot took the letters, shuffling them like a mailman as he went toward his desk. The Abbot sat, spreading the letters, opening them with a paper knife, reading with attention. As Kinsella tried to "read" him, noticing first, below the heavy brown woolen robe, black farmer's boots, with double leather soles, great hobnail cleats, and white woolen socks, their tops folded over the tops of these formidable boots. Of course the monks would not wear sandals in this cold. And, similarly, there were fisherman's black oilskins and a fisherman's sou'wester hat, hung up behind the Abbot's door. Those boots; that hat. A practical man. His hands, clumsy on the pages of the Ecumenical Order of Mission, were a workingman's hands, scaled with old cuts, the nails double-thick, blue-edged. Thin neck, large, glottal Adam's apple, moving in the socket of an oversize collar. The Abbot's grizzled hair was cut very short and, with gray eyes set far back in his skull, separated from his weathered face by a web of white frown lines, he had the look of a sea bird, a fisher hawk, perhaps. Yet, as he put the Ecumenical Order aside and began, attentively, to read the General's letter, Kinsella thought he saw something else. There was, in this humbly dressed old monk, a presence, a power, which recalled to his visitor a painting seen in Venice: Bastiani's portrait of Doge Francesco Foscari, mercantile noble, consummate politician. No, this would not be easy.

"A red-letter day," the Abbot said cheerfully, holding the General's letter up, the better to read it in the window light. "I have been an Albanesian monk for forty-five years, yet this is the first time I've ever held in my hand the signature of our Father General. A red-letter day, indeed. A pity it has to be a letter of censure."

"It is not meant as such, I can assure you."

"I agree. The tone is not unkind," the Abbot said. "But if you have attention paid to you from headquarters and you in a place like this, well, it's a fair guess that you're in hot water."

Kinsella laughed.

"Do you know of what we call a place like this, in Ireland? The back of beyond. That's where you are now. The back of beyond."

"It's a great phrase."

"Mind you," the Abbot said. "A few hundred years ago, no place in Christendom was the back of beyond. The Pope, in those days, had a very long arm, indeed. I'll show you something that turned up out in the back there, twenty years ago, in a heap of stuff that was stored away and

forgotten. It might amuse you. I mean, the container."
The Abbot tugged at the side drawer of his desk. It
opened with an unused squeal. Took from the drawer a
flat tin on which was a colored picture of a bearded
British sailor of former times. And a legend: *Player's Navy
Cut Cigarettes.* "In the days when a lot of people smoked
cigarettes—fags, they called them in Ireland—we had an
old lay brother, he was very fond of a smoke, and so,
when he found this, he thought he was made. 'Fifty fags,
Father,' said he to me, pleased as Punch with himself.
And so,"—the Abbot opened the box—"when he opened it
up, lo and behold, this was what was in it." The Abbot
took out a something, wrapped in tissue paper. He un-
wrapped it, showing a wax seal. "Have a look at that."

Kinsella took the seal, handling it gently as a sand dollar.
Traced in brown wax, the letters:

P I U S

P A P A

I I

"In fourteen sixty-three, that seal came here on a letter.
We had someone look up the date for us in Rome. In that
year Pope Pius the Second wrote to Walter Tobar, the
Abbot of Muck, and told him there was a deanship in
Kerry reported to be held by a man who had no canonical
title. The Pope wanted the Abbot to jump on the man and
teach him a lesson. And the Abbot did what he was told."

Laughter, which became a fit of coughing. "So, you see
when the word comes this far down the line it usually
means trouble for somebody or other. Eh, Father?"

Kinsella smiled and carefully handed back the seal. The
Abbot shut it in the tin box. "Cup of tea?"

"Oh, no thanks."

Irishly, the Abbot appraised this, and, Irishly, decided
the denial was mere politeness. "Ah, you will!" the Abbot
said. He called downstairs. "Brother Martin?"

"Aye."

"Bring us a cup of tea, will you?"

"Two teas," Martin's voice rumbled from below. The

Abbot, this settled, again picked up Father General's letter. "I am the sort of person who has to read everything important at least twice over."

"Go ahead."

As the Abbot reread, Kinsella stared about the room. The parlor was large, with high ceiling, located somewhere over the abbey's sacristy. Three narrow windows gave onto the sea. The furniture, carved by monks, was serviceable, without style. The walls were shelved by books, hundreds of them, spilling onto tables and stacked in odd corners. Surprisingly, there was a special table covered with old green paperback Penguin mystery stories. On the wall, to the Abbot's right, were three stone panels, seventeenth-century Celtic, saints or apostles, figures of beauty, their simplicity emphasized by a horrid oil which took pride of place behind the Abbot's desk, a Victorian painting of a ship sailing in a storm-tossed sea, under heavens rent by the Virgin Mary, prayerful, in blue and white robes, imploring her Heavenly Son for the vessel's safety.

On a window ledge, five large, wooden games boxes, each labeled in italic script:

> *Chess (I)*
> *Chess (II)*
> *Draughts (2 sets)*
> *Dominoes (I)*
> *Dominoes (incomplete)*

"Do you have television here?"

The Abbot paused in his rereading. "Sometimes, when there is something big happening in the world, we draw lots and five of us bicycle across the island to Doran's shop on the strand. They have television there."

A pause.

"Not more than five of us, though. Doran's is a small place."

"You know, of course, Father Abbot, that the Mass on Mount Coom and the pilgrims who come to Cahirciveen were widely publicized on a B.B.C. television program, a couple of months ago."

"Indeed I do. Didn't we get hundreds of letters about it.

I had no notion the Latin Mass was so popular. Do you know, it has given us a new penance. When one of us accuses himself of error before the chapter, he now has to answer some of those letters."

Footsteps. Stout, stertorous, Brother Martin emerged from the stairwell. On a wooden tray were two heavy china bowls, the size of soup bowls. They were filled with strong tea. Milk, sugar, a knife, a pot of blackberry jam. And two plates, each with a thick slice of white bread.

"Did you want an egg with that?" Brother Martin asked, putting the tray down on the Abbot's desk.

"No. We're having salmon with our supper, if Brother Manus can find a few in the pool."

"*Salmon?*"

"Yes, salmon. Father Kinsella has come all the way from Rome. This is an occasion, Martin."

Brother Martin turned to Kinsella. "That bread is our own baking. Irish soda bread." He went back downstairs.

"Poor Martin, he's getting on. We all are, here. I remember, last year, I said to Father Matthew, our master of novices, I said when you retire, we will retire your job with you. For not one recruit did I see coming along. But, do you know, after that television program, we had all sorts of inquiries. I tell you, I could recruit enough young men now to fill a regiment."

"I suppose that's a relief."

"A relief?" The Abbot paused, staring over the rim of his tea bowl. He held the bowl, his index finger cupped over its lip, in the eighteenth-century manner.

"I mean the prospect of being able to get recruits."

"It is not," the Abbot said, putting down his tea bowl and addressing himself to bread and jam.

"You are not anxious for new recruits?"

"I am not. It is a hard life on this island. Fishing, drying kelp, farming a few potatoes. It rains a lot. The monastery is a cold place, there is no way of heating it properly. And we are often hard put to make ends meet."

"But, isn't that the thing about hardship? I mean, men will accept it, if they feel it's for a worthwhile cause."

"Just so." The Abbot spread blackberry jam on his bread. "But the monastic life, as you know yourself, Father, is often something else. I'd break all clergy into two groups. Proselytizers, or prayers. Or, if you like, missionaries or monks."

"Monks can also be missionaries, surely?"

"Not on Muck Island. It takes a special vocation to live in a place like this. Not many have it. I do not have it myself, I sometimes think."

"But you have lived on this island most of your adult life?"

"That does not mean I like it."

"You'd prefer to be somewhere else?"

"I did not say that."

"I'm sorry. Of course not."

"This blackberry jam," the Abbot said, "is last year's. Brother Paul is down in the calefactory room now, bottling this year's jam. He is thinking of his jam. He is not thinking of anything else. I would say Brother Paul has a true vocation for this life."

Kinsella bit into his bread. "And it's delicious jam."

"It is."

"I suppose I am the missionary type," Kinsella said. "My great desire was to be sent to South America."

"Ah, Father Gustav Hartmann. A fine man he must be."

"He is."

"So you went to South America?"

"No. But I studied with Father Hartmann in his class in Boston. He's crippled now, you know."

"No. I did not know."

"He was tortured so many times. The *pau de arara*. Finally, the Brazilian *militares* broke his back."

"I would like to meet him," the Abbot said. "Tell me, does he talk much about God?"

"In what way do you mean, Father Abbot?"

"Ah, I don't know. Forget it. No, what I mean is," the Abbot paused, as though thinking, "is it souls he's after? Or is it the good of mankind?"

"I would say the second."

The Abbot nodded. "I gathered as much. Of course, I'm not well up on such things. I never had the missionary impulse myself."

"But your zeal for the old Mass, your continuance of the

Latin ritual, surely that could be interpreted as missionary spirit?"

"I thought you'd get around to that," the Abbot said, and laughed. "Come on. Let's take a turn outside. The rain has stopped and I want to order up that salmon for our supper. You'll stay the night?"

Kinsella hesitated.

"Ah, you will! What did you tell the man with the helicopter?"

"I said I would telephone him when I'm ready to leave. He can get here in about an hour."

"Time enough, then, to ring him in the morning." The Abbot stood and took his oilskins and sou'wester from the hook behind the door. "Mind the step as you go down."

At the foot of the staircase, a door led to the sacristy. They went through and emerged in the cloister. The Abbot moved briskly, his hobnailed boots loud on the flags of the walk, turning up through a slype and into the refectory, a large bare room around the walls of which were rough refectory tables and benches. In the adjoining kitchen two old monks peeled potatoes from a huge pile. On the hearth hung an iron pot, big as a cartoon cannibal's cookpot. The turf fire gave off a pleasant scent.

One of the old monks looked up and smiled at the visitor. He had two upper teeth, it seemed. "G'day" said he. " 'Twill clear, I would say."

"Ah, yes," said the other old monk.

"Where is Father Manus?"

"I hear tell he's looking for a couple of fish," one old monk said. The other giggled.

"Right, then," the Abbot said. "We'll go and see what he's got."

A door, heavy and stiff on its iron hinges, swung open and they were outside, on a slope of field, looking down at those gray rocks, that splendor of sea. Below, a path led to a small cove. Four black curraghs lay upended on a shelf of rock. A man, in oilskins, carrying a fishing creel, could be seen trudging slowly along the strand. "Come on, down," the Abbot said to his guest. "I think that's our fish."

As they went down the path—"The man with that creel is Father Manus, a very good soul. He is the priest who said the Mass that Sunday when the television fellows came. The other monks make fun of him, now. The reporters tried to interview him on the television but he wouldn't speak." The Abbot kicked a stone clear of the path. "He will speak to you, never fear. He's dying to get a chance at you, I warn you. Still, that's what you're here for, I suppose. Explanations, wasn't that what Father General called them?"

"Yes."

"Maaaaa-nus! Did you get a fish?"

Shouting, his voice lifted and lost in the wind. Implacable, the loud sea on gray-green rocks. The man in oilskins heard, held up his creel.

"We have our fish," the Abbot said.

"Good."

"When Manus catches a salmon he puts it in an ocean pool and the next day, when the boat goes over, we sell on the mainland. Salmon gets a big price. So tonight is a special treat. Eating salmon ourselves. It's things like that—" the Abbot turned on the path and looked back up, his fisher-hawk's eyes searching Kinsella's face—"it's the little things that keep us going, here. Like the jam I was talking about. Do you follow me? That is the jam in our lives."

Then turned and went on down, a heavy old man in black oilskins, his head hidden by the sou'wester hat.

While the needs of your particular congregation might seem to be served by retention of the Latin Mass, nevertheless, as Father Kinsella will explain to you, your actions in continuing to employ the older form are, at this time, particularly susceptible to misinterpretation elsewhere as a deliberate contravention of the spirit of aggiornamento. *Such an interpretation can and will be made, not only within the councils of the Church itself, but within the larger councils of the ecumenical movement. This is particularly distressful to us at this time, in view of the* apertura, *possibly the most significant historical event of our century, when interpenetration between Christian and Buddhist faiths is on the verge of reality.*

For all of these reasons, in conclusion, I will only say that, while Father Kinsella is with you to hear

*explanations, be it understood his decision is mine
and, as such, is irrevocable.*

English was not, of course, Father General's first language. *Explanations* was an unfortunate choice of word.
Kinsella watched the Abbot jump from rock to shore,
landing heavily but surely, striding across the rain-damp
sand to meet the other monk, whose habit hung down
soaking beneath his black oilskin coat. I would be angered
by the tone of that last paragraph. And this is an abbot
who ignored his own provincial for a dozen years. What
if he ignores me? In Brazil, when the Bishop of Manáos
denounced Hartmann as a false priest, he was banished
from the city and, upriver, the villagers refused him food.
But he stayed, eating wild roots, waiting in the rain forest
until he had sapped the bishop's power. What could *I* do
in this godforsaken spot?

"Hey!"

The other monk, grinning, held open his creel as the
Abbot drew close. Three large salmon, silver-scaled, on a
bed of green moss. Grinning, arrested as though in
some long-ago school snapshot, the old monk seemed,
somehow, to have retained the awkward, boyish grace of
his adolescent days.

"Well, Father Abbot, and how will these suit you?" he
said, then turned to nod and grin at Kinsella, as though
inviting him to share an enormous and obvious joke.

"They will do," the Abbot said, playing his part with great
deliberation as he held the creel up. "Yes, I will say they
will do nicely, Manus. And this is Father Kinsella, all the
way from Rome. Father Manus, our champion fisherman."

"Hello, there," Kinsella said.

"From Rome? So you're the man from Rome. I'd never
have thought it."

"What were you expecting?"

"Well, somebody older. A real sergeant major. And most
likely an Italian, or something on that order. You're
American, are you?"

"I am."

"Anyway, I'm delighted to see you. Oh, God forgive
me, I'm not delighted at all. Sure we're all in fear and
trembling of what you're going to do here."

"Manus!" The Abbot, amused, hit Father Manus a thump between the shoulderblades. "Hold your tongue, man. Aren't you the alpha and the omega? When Manus was a little boy they told him it was a sin to tell a lie. I do believe he has not committed that sin since."

"Ah, but seriously, Father Kinsella," Father Manus said. "I have to talk to you. I mean it is an astonishing thing that's happened here. I go over to the mainland every Sunday. And you should just see the way the people react."

"It's beginning to rain," the Abbot warned. "If you want to talk to Father Kinsella, I'd suggest we do it inside. Come along, now."

Setting a brisk pace, he turned and led them back up the path from the beach. The heavy monastery door shut stiffly behind them as they regained the cloister. First to the kitchen, where Father Manus handed over the fish to the old kitchen monks. Then, the Abbot beckoning, Father Manus and Kinsella were led into a small room, furnished with draftsman's tables and high stools. "All right," the Abbot said. "I'll be referee. Now, Manus, here's your chance. Have at him. What was it you were going to say?"

"What was it I wanted to tell him? What was it I wanted, ah, Lord, I do not know, I tell you, Father Kinsella, since I heard you were coming, I have lain awake at night arguing the toss with myself, saying this and saying that, and—look, it is as plain as the nose on your face, we did nothing to start all this, we went on saying the Mass over there in Cahirciveen the way it was always said, the way we had always said it, the way we had been brought up to say it. The Mass! The Mass in Latin, the priest with his back turned to the congregation because both he and the congregation faced the altar where God was. Offering up the daily sacrifice of the Mass *to God*. Changing bread and wine into the body and blood of Jesus Christ the way Jesus told his disciples to do it at the Last Supper. 'This is my body and this is my blood. Do ye this in commemoration of me.' God sent His Son to redeem us. His Son came down into the world and was crucified for our sins and the Mass is the commemoration of that crucifixion, of that sacrifice of the body and blood of Jesus Christ for our sins. It is priest and people praying to God, assisting in a miracle whereby Jesus Christ again comes down among us, body and blood in the form of the bread and wine there on the altar. And the Mass was said in Latin because Latin was the language of the Church and the Church was one and universal and a Catholic could go into any church in the world, here or in Timbuktu, or in China, and hear the same Mass, the only Mass there was, the Latin Mass. And if the Mass was in Latin and people did not speak Latin, that was part of the mystery of it, for the Mass was not talking to your neighbor, it was talking to God. Almighty God! And we did it that way for nearly two thousand years and, in all that time, the church was a place to be quiet in, and respectful, it was a hushed place because God was there, God on the altar, in the tabernacle in the form of a wafer of bread and a chalice of wine. It was God's house, where, every day, the daily miracle took place. God coming down among us. A mystery. Just as this new Mass isn't a mystery, it's a mockery, a singsong, it's not talking to God, it's talking to your neighbor, and that's why it's in English, or German or Chinese or whatever language the people in the church happen to speak. It's a symbol, they say, but a symbol of what? It's some entertainment show, that's what it is. And the people see through it. They do! That's why they come to Coom Mountain, that's why they come on planes and boats and the cars thick on the roads and the people camping out in the fields, God help them, and that's why they are there with the rain pouring down on them, and when the Sanctus bell is rung at the moment of the Elevation, when the priest kneels and raises up the Host—aye, that little round piece of bread that is now the body of Our Blessed Saviour—holds it up—Almighty God —and the congregation is kneeling at the priest's back, bowed down to adore their God, aye, Father, if you saw those people, their heads bare, the rain pelting off their faces, when they see the Host raised up, that piece of unleavened bread that, through the mystery and the miracle of the Mass, is now the body and blood of Jesus Christ, Our Saviour, then you would be ashamed, Father, you would be ashamed to sweep all that away and put in its place what you *have* put there—singing and guitars

and turning to touch your neighbor, play-acting and non-
sense, all to make the people come into church the way
they used to go to the parish hall for a bingo game!"

Clear: the challenge. His eyes rage-bright, a tiny froth
of spittle on his cheek as, confused, he came full stop in
his tirade. The Abbot stepped between adversaries. "I
wish I had all that fire and conviction, Manus. As for you,
Father Kinsella, you've just found out we have a lot of
sermons in us, here at the back of beyond."

"I'm sorry." Father Manus stared at Kinsella as he
would at a man he had, unexpectedly, punched in the
mouth. "But, still and all, what I said is only God's truth.
Father Abbot will bear me out."

"*I* don't know what God's truth is," the Abbot said.
"Do any of us? If we did, there would be no arguments
between us. But it *is* true that a lot of people seem to
feel the way Manus does about the old Mass. You know
that, of course. That is why you're here."

"Anyway," Father Manus said, his voice loud again,
"I think it would be a crime against the people's faith, if
we were forced to give up the old way here."

"Manus," the Abbot said, gently, "I wonder would you
ask Father Colum to start benediction. I would like to
show Father Kinsella around. Would you do that now, like
a good man?"

"Yes, Father Abbot, I will do that directly."

"You'll see each other again, at suppertime," the Abbot
promised.

Impulsively Father Manus caught hold of Kinsella's
arm. "There was nothing personal, Father."

"I know. I appreciate hearing your point of view."

A very dirty monk, face and hands stained with earth,
appeared at the door, unaware that he was interrupting.
"We found the lamb!" he shouted, then stared slack-
mouthed at the visitor.

"Good man yourself," the Abbot said. "Where was it?"

"But that's the story of it. In an old byre, by the ruin
where the Cullens used to live. And lying down, keeping
warm, up against a wee pony."

"With a pony?"

"Right forenenst it. A wee pony of Taig Murtagh's."

"And the pony didn't mind?"

"Divil a bit."

"There's the power of prayer for you," Father Manus said, his good humor restored.

"It took more than prayer," said the dirty monk. "It took the whole day."

"Go along now," the Abbot ordered, and the dirty monk went off with Father Manus. "Are you interested in Romanesque?" the Abbot asked Kinsella.

"Very much."

"Well, I'll show you a couple of things, then. Coming from Rome you will be hard to impress. Oh, what grand sights! I was there at the time of Pope John, years ago, may he rest in peace."

"To study?"

"Ah, no. Just on a holiday. I had been sick and so I was sent off on a jaunt. I went to London, then to Rome and on to Lourdes, in France. My first and last visit to the Continent, I expect."

"You enjoyed it."

"Oh, I had a grand time. It was grand to see England again. I served my novitiate there, in Buckmore Abbey in Kent."

"I know."

"Ah, yes, sure you probably know all about me. They make you do your homework well, there on the Lungotevere Vaticano?"

Kinsella, smiling, shook his head. Walking now between cloister arches, abbot and stranger, the object of constant, covert curiosity. Monks, mediating or reading their office, paced the covered walk, in silence. A light drizzle of rain fell in the rectangular cloister garth. These monks; this place. Most of them would know no other.

Hartmann, in class, sitting in his specially built orthopedic chair, by the window overlooking the Charles River in Boston, his eyes peering down, shaded by thick freckled fingers. There was a two-man skiff on the water below. "The key," Hartmann said, "was when we discovered that no one, or almost no one, in the entire hierarchy of Brazil, Chile, Argentina—no one was truly happy with his posting or his position

> *—once we grasped that truth, we could unlock any*
> *door. See that skiff down there? I will bet that one of*
> *those two rowers believes that the other man has the*
> *better seat. I would bet my life on it. Sometimes to*
> *force an issue, you have to bet your life on things like*
> *that—things you know nothing about."*

"This way," the Abbot said, leading him into the church. Now, standing in the nave of the Abbey, Kinsella felt again that sudden, vivid emotion, that elation in silence of the great bare church at Vézelay, most beautiful of all French Romanesque abbeys, greater even than Autun. Here, as in Vézelay, on this remote Irish island on the edge of the Gothic world, that hush, that bareness which contains all the beauty of belief. Above him, gray stone rose to arch in the Gothic symbol of hands joined in prayer. As in Vézelay, it was an edifice empty as silence, grave as grace. In the chancel, the altar, a bare stone slab on which stood a small tabernacle with a door of beaten Irish gold. Two wooden candlesticks were its only ornaments. No second altar, Kinsella noticed, nothing to conform with the liturgical change of 1966. In the south transept, a small shrine to the Virgin and, above the main altar, a Romanesque crucifix, high on the chancel wall, starveling stone Christ, hung on nails on cross of Irish bog oak.

The Abbot's boots were loud in the nave. "Twelfth century, most of it. But this doorway and these windows are thirteenth century, a transition from Irish Romanesque to Gothic. This cross motif is similar to that in the Monastery of Cong, a Cistercian house. But this one is finer. Probably the finest in Ireland, they tell us."

"It is beautiful."

"A big church this, when you think of the place it's in. Of course there used to be more families living on Muck. The main construction is the original structure. There used to be a holy well on the island, at the time those things were popular. People came over from the mainland by boat to visit it. Little rowboats, made of skin and wood frames, coracles they were called. *Those* people had faith."

"Buckmore is a beautiful abbey too, I hear?"

The Abbot twisted around, head cocked oddly to one side. "It is. Different, of course. This abbey is older and has never been burned. It's one of the few in Ireland that escaped both Henry the Eighth and Cromwell. There are advantages to being remote."

Before leaving Rome, remembering Hartmann's advice in class, Kinsella had mentioned to Father General the question of a transfer. "Sometimes a more rewarding posting brings about a great change of heart," Kinsella said. Father General agreed. "But, only as a last resort. Use it, if absolutely necessary."

"The other thing I wanted to show you is up there in the south transept," the Abbot said. "Come this way." Genuflecting, moving past benches where four monks knelt in prayer, heads cowled, faces hidden. "All of the Abbots of Muck are buried under this wall. Every one. Can you imagine that? As far as we know, it goes back to the founding. According to the records there are fifty-one laid down there, like bottles of wine. And, God willing, I'll be fifty-two. It's rare having abbots laid down like that. Our abbey in Santiago de Compostola is the only other one I've heard of that has this sort of arrangement."

"If you were appointed Abbot elsewhere, would they not send your body back here to be buried?"

"No. The rule holds only if the Abbot dies here. I'd say my chance is very good. I hope so, anyway. It's an idiotic sort of ambition, but I have it. Funny. This island is not exactly a summer resort, but, do you know, if I go out on the mainland now, I'll not sleep one night over there, if I can get back in. I feel at home here. I am at home nowhere else."

Kinsella stared at his host. Transfer foreseen and forestalled. Did this abbot leave nothing to chance? And now, as though continuing a guided tour, the Abbot led him away, as monks in twos and threes, cowled, came in at every door until, some twenty-five, they filled the two front benches. From the sacristy, a priest emerged in a cope, silk and gold cloth, richly embroidered by nuns long dead. Before him, a lay brother with censer and chain. *Benediction.* The Abbot, hurrying his guest from this scene of irregularity, pushed open a heavy door in the side of the nave. They went out under rain-dark skies.

"We have a little guest house, it's not very grand, but there is a hot tub. We'll have our supper at seven. That will give us plenty of time afterwards, if you want to have a chat."

"Thank you."

Following the Abbot along a mud-edged path under the west wall of the monastery toward a building like a large outhouse alone in a field. "It's off on its own, as you can see." The Abbot turned a key in the door. Inside, a small hall, with an unlit turf fire set in the grate. A coat hanger, a visitor's book on a wooden table, and, on the whitewashed wall, a crucifix made of woven reeds. Off the hall was a bedroom with a narrow monk's bed, a wooden chair, a sheepskin rug on the floor. The bathroom, adjoining, was primitive but adequate; tub, washbasin, toilet, all in a tiny space.

"We will pick you up at six-fifteen. If you are cold, just put a match to that fire."

The door shut. Kinsella moved like a prisoner in the cell-like rooms, then, deciding, stripped off his clothes and ran water in the old-fashioned bathtub. Lay in the tub, the steamy water blurring mirror and windowpane, listening to the cry of gulls, mind idling as his body, gentled by the warm water, grew slack and at ease. The Abbot seemed to be in charge. Father Manus had, no doubt, been brought in early, to dispose of the emotional appeal. There were probably others of his persuasion here. The Abbot used Father Manus to say what he himself is too shrewd to say. Father General's letter is what really interests him; he read it at least three times. He is not angling for preferment or power. Reasonable in what he says; captain of his ship. If this letter from the owners tells him to dump a cargo of ritual, my guess is he will do as he is bid. Hartmann, looking down at the two-man skiff on the Charles River, saying one must be prepared to gamble everything on a hunch. Will I gamble on the Abbot if he gives me his word? Or is there a gray eminence here, a *Mann im Schatten* I have not yet faced?

Kinsella rose, dripping, from the tub. In the evening air,

already cool, the room misted like a steam bath. The towel was rough on his skin. He thought of the confessions: no one had mentioned the confessions. They were, he knew, the greatest danger.

FORTY MINUTES LATER, when the knock came on the door, he was waiting, dressed in his gray-green fatigues and his flying jacket. Old, grinning schoolboy face, hand clasping his sou'wester, keeping it firm on long gray locks, Father Manus entered the hall, scraping mud clots from the soles of his boots. "Terrible wind! I asked if I could come for you. I am heartsick."

"What?"

"I offered up prayers at Benediction in penance for shouting at you like some wild man from Borneo. As Father Abbot pointed out, sure, I never gave you a chance to open your mouth."

"That's all right."

"It is not all right. It's a disgrace." Father Manus blushed from the neck up, turning to hide his embarrassment, peering out at the gusty rain. "Pelting down. We'll have to run for it. They are all waiting to meet you in the ref."

Slamming the guest house door, Kinsella kept close to his guide, half running, until they reached the monastery gate. Hurried along the cloister walk to the refectory where the community was assembled, clustered in twos and threes like conference delegates, all whispers and shy smiles as Father Manus led the visitor in. Coats were taken and hung up. The Abbot came forward, genial, linking Kinsella's arm, leading him around, introducing him.

"Father John, Father Colum, Brother Kevin. And Brother Sean. Father Kinsella, from Rome. An Irish name that is? Yes. Is it true what we heard, that Padraig refused to take you on his boat this morning? It is? Oh, glory be! And Father Terence, Father Kinsella from Rome. Terence is in charge of our farm here. Father Alphonsus, Father Kinsella. Did you come all the way from Rome now in that whirligig that landed here today? All the way from Rome, oh, did you hear what Father Alphonsus wants to know! Ah, for goodness' sake, don't you know that's a helicopter, it could not fly all the way from Rome. Ah, so you came in a bigger airplane, did you? I see. From Amsterdam to Shannon and then from Shannon by car. And the helicopter was only because of Padraig. So that was the way of it. Do you know, Father Kinsella, I hear tell there is not a village in Ireland that does not have some class of an airfield nearby. Isn't that amazing. Yes, yes.

"And this is Father Matthew, our master of novices. What novices are you talking about, Father Abbot, I think it would be better to introduce me as jack of all trades and master of none. Hardly so, Father Matthew. Anyway, I want you to meet Father Kinsella, from Rome. Indeed, I know he is from Rome. We all do. You are here because of the doings at Cahirciveen, isn't that so? Yes. It is wonderful the response of the people there on Mount Coom. Wonderful. It would do your heart good to see the piety of the ordinary people. Indeed it would. And I hope —by the way, have you met Father Daniel?—Father Daniel, Father Kinsella. Father Daniel is our business manager. Excuse me, Father Matthew, you were saying? I was saying I hope you are not planning to change our ways, Father Kinsella. In what way, Father Matthew? The Mass, Father. I will be honest and tell you I have been saying a novena for weeks now, hoping that we will be allowed to go on with this holy work."

The Abbot, smooth, led his visitor from danger. "If Father Kinsella would sit here, on my right? And this is Father Walter, my deputy. Sit on Father Kinsella's right, will you, Father Walter, that way we'll have him surrounded by the Muck Island Establishment, haha." Great noise of refectory benches as twenty-six monks sat in to supper. All waited. The Abbot rang a handbell. At once all eyes went to the kitchen door as the two old cook brothers, faces full in triumphal smiles, brought the salmon in. Three fish on three white china platters. Then, great bowls of steaming boiled potatoes. Salt and butter dishes. Three big pitchers of buttermilk. When the food was on the table, the Abbot stood. All stood. All prayed:

"Bless us, O Lord, and these Thy gifts, which, of Thy bounty, we are about to receive, through Christ, Our Lord, Amen." Not, Kinsella noted, the approved Ecumenical grace, standard in all other monasteries of the

Order. Afterwards, in continuing anachronism, all made the Sign of the Cross. All sat. The Abbot served his guest, then himself. The platters were passed. All ate in silence, quickly, heads bowed to their food. It was the old rule. When the Abbot rose, all rose. "We give Thee thanks, O Lord, for all Thy benefits, Who livest and reignest, world without end. Amen. May the souls of the faithful departed, through the mercy of God, rest in peace. Amen."

Afterwards, the community hovered respectfully, hoping to engage the visitor in further conversation. But the Abbot did not linger. "We will go up now to my parlor for a cup of tea. We are early to bed and early to rise here. Fishermen and farmers of a sort, as we are, we must use the light God gives us. So, if you will come this way, Father?"

"Good night. Good night. Off so soon? Good night, Father. Sleep well." They watched him go, cheated by this abrupt departure: they had few visitors. Their long-skirted lines parted in polite reluctance as the Abbot, purposeful, led Kinsella back through the cloister, into the sacristy, and up the winding stone staircase to the parlor.

On the Abbot's desk, Brother Martin had left a pot of tea and, incongruously, a plate of lemon puff biscuits. The Abbot took one of the biscuits, holding it up between forefinger and thumb. "Martin is trying to bribe you," he said. "Whenever he wants to soften somebody up, he parts with a few of these. His married sister sends them to him, all the way from Manchester." He munched the biscuit and, munching, moved to pick up the Ecumenical Order of Mission. Frowning, he read it once again. "Sit down, Father. Make yourself comfortable." The Ecumenical Order was tossed on the desk, discarded. Again the General's letter. Read, how many times now? Reread again, then held up, as though in exhibit. "Is there something I could say that might change your, and our Father General's, opinion of these events?"

"Well, I wouldn't know, would I? As you haven't said anything yet."

The Abbot laughed as though this were some extremely subtle joke. "Do you know what they are calling you, over there in the refectory, Father?"

Kinsella waited, smiling at his host.

"The inquisitor." The Abbot laughed. "I thought that was good."

"Hardly an inquisitor."

"Why not? Didn't the Inquisition come around to seek out doctrinal error and punish it?"

"My mission is not punitive."

"Not yet. But what if the heresy continues?"

"Look," Kinsella said, slightly irritated. "This is the end of the twentieth century, not the beginning of the thirteenth. How can we even define what heresy is today?"

"Yesterday's orthodoxy is today's heresy."

"I wouldn't say that, Father Abbot."

"Then what have you got against us saying the Mass in the old way?"

"We are trying to create a uniform posture within the Church. If everyone decides to worship in his own way—well, it's obvious, it would create a disunity."

"Exactly," the Abbot said. "Breakdown. The loss of control. Look, I agree. There must be discipline. Dish of tea?"

"Thank you, yes."

"Milk and sugar?"

"Black."

The Abbot poured and passed the bowl of tea to his guest. "Explanations," the Abbot said. "Father General seems to feel they would be in order. Very well. I will try to explain why we kept the old Mass here. Will I tell you why?"

"Yes, I would like it—yes, please do."

"Did you know that Ireland used to be the only country in Europe where every Catholic went to Mass of a Sunday? Everyone, even the men?"

"Yes. I was here some years ago. In Sligo."

"Were you, now? Well, anyway, when this new Mass came in, we tried it, we did what we were told. But we noticed that the men would come into Cahirciveen with their families and stand, smoking and talking, outside the church. When Mass was over, they took their women home. Now, I thought that was a bad sign. I mean, this is Ireland, after all. I wrote our Father Provincial about it.

He wrote back that the new Mass was popular everywhere else. Well, I did not know what to do. We were losing our congregation, hand over fist. I said to myself, maybe the people here are different from the people in other places, maybe they will not stand for this change. After all, what are we doing, playing at being Sunday priests over there on the mainland, if it's not trying to keep the people's faith in Almighty God? I am not a holy man, but maybe because I am not, I felt I had no right to interfere. I thought it was my duty, not to disturb the faith they have. So, I went back to the old way."

"Then what happened?"

"Nothing happened."

"But it must have been noticed. There must have been talk in the diocese?"

"I suppose there was. But people are not well informed on liturgical matters. I think the people thought because we are an old order we had some special dispensation to do things the old way. Anyway, the old way became very popular, after the word got around."

"And, soon, you had thousands coming to Mass every Sunday."

"That is not so," the Abbot said. "For a number of years we did not have many extra people. Some older people from parishes about. But it was just lately it caught on. It was the tourists. Ireland is choked with tourists now in the summer months. I blame those new planes, those supers, or whatever you call them."

"So, it was only last summer that you moved out of the priory in Cahirciveen and began saying Mass on Mount Coom?"

"You are well informed. I am not surprised. Our Father Provincial, in Dublin, is not what you would call an admirer of mine."

"On Mount Coom," Kinsella said. "You decided to say Mass on the Mass rock. According to my reading, the Mass rock, in Penal times, was associated with rebellion. Mass was said there, by outlaw priests, in secret, with some member of the congregation on the lookout in case the English soldiers came."

"The Mass rock was a mistake," the Abbot said. "At

the time I did not think of the connection. I was just trying to accommodate the crowds."

"You accepted a gift of loudspeakers from the merchants of Cahirciveen."

"It is customary to accept gifts which aim at enhancing worship."

"But, loudspeakers," Kinsella said. "Surely, it has occurred to you that Mount Coom has become a place of pilgrimage?"

"Do you mean a sort of Lourdes?"

"As Lourdes used to be. Lourdes is no longer in operation."

"We are not at all like Lourdes. There are no miracles. We just say Mass."

"And hear private confessions. Which is not known even now, in Rome. I only found it out by accident, myself, the other day in Cahirciveen. As you know, private confessions have been abolished, except in cases of special need where the sin is so grave that private counsel is necessary."

The Abbot frowned. "All mortal sins are mortal to the soul. I find these new rulings difficult to apply."

"To begin with, as you know, the category of mortal or venial sin is no longer in use."

"But what am I to do?" The Abbot seemed suddenly distraught. "The people here still think it is a special sin to molest a child, to steal a man's wife, to marry in sin— ah—a whole lot of things! What am I to do if the people still believe that sin is mortal?"

"I know it must be difficult. But the retention of private confessions would be a serious mistake. Now that the easier form has been sanctioned by Vatican IV—you have read the debates, surely?"

"I have, indeed," the Abbot said. "I know that I am not in step, in the matter of confessions. But, remember, I tried to limit the confessions to people from our parish. It was all part of the same thing. We did not want to disturb the faith of the local people. Still . . ." The Abbot paused and looked searchingly at his visitor. "You said yourself that Rome did not know about the private confessions. You were not sent here because of that?"

"No."

"Why were you sent, Father Kinsella? What, in particular, caused this—?" The Abbot picked up Father General's letter.

"American television is planning to do a special one-hour program on what has happened here. Did you know that?"

"So that's it!" The Abbot made a fist of his right hand and hit the top of his desk. "The damned television! I did not want television here. I will ban them. I was dead against it from the start."

"Even the President of the United States can't ban American television. If the networks want to televise what's going on here, it will be done. And it will be seen all over the world."

"I warned our monks and I told the merchants at Cahirciveen the self-same thing, I said don't have anything to do with those telly people, just tell them it's none of their concern. I refused them permission for any filming on Church property."

"It didn't do much good, did it? Don't you see that even your action in refusing to let these ceremonies be filmed can lend a significance to them that you never intended? A program in the wrong hands, about this subject, could be made to look like the first stirrings of a Catholic counterrevolution."

"Ah, now begging your pardon, Father Kinsella, I find that very far-fetched."

"Far-fetched? To the enemies of the Church, won't it seem that you have acted in direct contradiction to the counsels of Vatican IV?"

The Abbot stared at the fire. In the reflected light of the flames, his features seemed gray as a plaster cast. "I didn't think of myself as contradicting Rome. God forbid."

"I am sure you didn't. And I have been sent here, simply, to clarify things. To explain Father General's concern. And to ask you, for the greater good, to stop this Mass, and these private confessions, at once."

The Abbot, hitching the skirts of his robe, leaned toward the fire, staring at the flames. Kinsella stood. He began to speak, a pulse trembling in his throat, his voice loud in the room, the voice of a believer, telling his true creed.

"Father General, in his letter, mentioned the *apertura* with Buddhism, which, of course, you've read about. Perhaps it seems to you that this has nothing to do with life here on this island, but, believe me, it has. Father General is president of the special Ecumenical Council which will inaugurate the Bangkok talks next month. It is the first time an Order head has been so chosen, and any scandal about the Albanesians at this time could, as you can guess, be extremely embarrassing to Father General at the talks. He was anxious that you understand he is in a very delicate stage of these negotiations. The *bonze* demonstrations at Kuala Lumpur are, we feel, only a beginning of the opposition tactics."

The Abbot swiveled in his chair, staring up at his visitor. He did not speak. Then, rising, he walked to the windows of his parlor. The faded light of an Irish summer's evening washed a late northern brightness into the room. Through narrow windowpanes, the Abbot stared at the sky. Gray storm clouds sailed west toward America. The sky, abandoned, was bled white by a hidden sun. "I envy you," the Abbot said. "I have been a priest for forty-odd years but I have never been sure why. It must be very rewarding to feel that one's actions might actually change something in this world of ours. If I ask you a question, I hope you won't be offended. But, when a young fellow like you kneels down in church, do you pray? Do you actually say prayers, things like the Hail Mary, the Our Father, and so on?"

"Are you asking me what do I believe?"

"Yes, if you wish. There is a book by a Frenchman called Francis Jeanson, have ever you heard of it? *An Unbeliever's Faith,* it is called."

"I have not read it."

"It is interesting. He believes there can be a future for Christianity, provided it gets rid of God. Your friend, Father Hartmann, has mentioned Jeanson in his own writings. The idea is, a Christianity that keeps God can no longer stand up to Marxism. You have not heard of the book?"

"Yes, I have heard of it," Kinsella said. "But, I have not read it."

"A pity. I wanted to ask you—the Mass, for instance. What is the Mass to you?"

Kinsella looked at the Abbot, as the Abbot stared out at the evening sky. Now was the time for truth, if only a cautious part of the truth. "I suppose, the Mass to me, as to most Catholics in the world today, is a symbolic act. I do not believe that the bread and wine on the altar is changed into the body and blood of Christ, except in a purely symbolic manner. Therefore, I do not, in the old sense, think of God as actually being present, there in the tabernacle."

The Abbot turned from the window, head cocked on one side, his hawk's features quizzical. "Isn't that remarkable," the Abbot said. "And yet you seem to be what I would call a very *dedicated* young man."

"In what way is it remarkable, Father Abbot? It's the standard belief, in this day and age."

"Or lack of belief," the Abbot said. "I think I was born before my time. A man doesn't have to have such a big dose of faith any more, does he?"

Kinsella smiled. "Perhaps not." He had been about to add that today's best thinking saw the disappearance of the church building as a place of worship in favor of a more generalized community concept, a group gathered in a meeting to celebrate God-in-others. But decided that, perhaps, the Abbot was not ready for that step.

"Yes," the Abbot said. "I see now why the old Mass is *non grata.* And why you're here to tell us to cease and desist."

"My job is, primarily, to explain the situation—including the special problems facing the Order at present—and, of course, to help handle any transitional problems which might arise with tourists or press."

"You mean when we give up the old Mass?"

"Yes."

"And if I choose to retain it?"

"I hope that won't be the case."

"But you are the General's plenipotentiary," the Abbot said. "If it *is* the case, then you have authority to act against me."

"Yes, I do."

"I don't know why I'm asking," the Abbot said. "The letter made that quite clear. I must be a glutton for punishment."

"On the contrary, you seem to me a very reasonable man. And as an Abbot, with episcopal powers, you realize better than I do the need for seniors in our Order to act in concert and set an example."

"Now, now, hold on, hold your horses," the Abbot said, smiling. "I've had a terrible lot of sermons thrown at me these last weeks. I know what you're going to say, and so on and so forth. But, right now, what I need to do is sit down and think about this letter from Father General. I believe I will do that. We can talk in the morning. Will that be all right?"

"Of course."

"We'll not keep you here forever, don't worry. Padraig will take you back to the mainland any time you want to go."

"Fine. No hurry."

The Abbot picked up the poker from the grate and hammered on the flagstones. "Martin?"

Below, a voice: "Yes, Father Abbot."

"Will you take our visitor to his quarters?"

Turned to Kinsella, holding out his hand. "Sleep well, Father. And thank you for coming to Muck. I'll be along to take you to breakfast in the morning. Would eight suit you?"

"Fine."

"Martin?"

"Yes, Father Abbot." Brother Martin was now at the head of the stairwell.

"Put a light on the west wall. Father Kinsella is not, like yourself, some class of a night cat."

Brother Martin laughed, as at an old joke. "This way, Father."

STERTOROUS, a noise like a man blowing on a fire to redden coals, why must they pick this overweight monk for the heart-hurting job of ascending and descending these winding turret stairs? Down, down, behind Brother Martin, gazing at the shiny tonsure on the back of his skull.

Through the musty camphor smell of the sacristy, into the cloister walk, Brother Martin by now wheezing in a frightening manner. At the west entrance an unoiled door opened with a scream of hinges and a monk, wearing a heavy frayed overcoat over his robe, his face half hidden by a full red beard, came out, beckoning. "Father Kinsella?"

"Yes."

"There was a telephone call for you."

"This is Brother Kevin," Brother Martin said.

" 'Twas a call from Dingle. The helicopter company. Did you want to ring them?"

"Maybe I'd better."

"Go along then, Martin. I'll take Father Kinsella back." Gripping Kinsella's arm. "Come in, come in."

And shut the screaming door. The room was like a bunker, a narrow window twelve feet long by two feet wide stretched along one wall, giving on a view of mountains, and a cove where curraghs were drawn up on the strand. Papers, manila folders, a short-wave radio, and a telephone were jumbled on a long wooden table. The walls were lined with red and white buoys, lobster creels, fishing tackle of various sorts.

"I admit it's a shambles," said the red-bearded monk, and now Kinsella recognized the crackly, humorous voice he had spoken to from the pub and from Hern's Hotel. "Will I get you Dingle?"

"Yes. Western Helicopters. Dingle Four-oh-two, I think."

"That's right. Dan Gavin runs that outfit. I know him." He cranked the handle. "Would you get us Dingle Four-oh-two, Sheilagh? Thanks, Sheilagh."

He turned to look at Kinsella. "Do the priests in Rome not dress like priests any more?"

"Clerical dress is optional, except on special occasions."

"That's a grand outfit *you're* wearing. Dashing! You look like a soldier boy."

The phone rang. The red-bearded monk handed over the receiver. Kinsella's pilot was on the line. "Yes, I called earlier, Father. We have a report that the island will be socked in around noon. Bad storm off the coast of Spain, coming up fast."

"By noon?"

"Yes. Mightn't even be able to get off by boat after that. Gale-force winds forecast for all of Kerry."

"I see." Held the phone, stared at by the red-bearded monk as, furious, his mind raced through a scenario. "All right," he said. "See if you can come in at nine, okay?"

"Same spot?"

"Right."

"Nine o'clock, then. Will do."

"Good night. And thank you."

Redbeard's lips went wide in a grin. "So you're leaving us in the morning, then?"

Kinsella smiled, but did not answer.

"Well, I suppose you'll be wanting to get back to your quarters. I'll show you the road. This way."

The door screamed. They went across the cloister and out at the west gate. Pre-darkness, a failing of light, dimmed the summer sky above them. The wind was strong, blowing the grasses flat along the edges of their muddy path. The red-bearded monk unlocked the guest house door. "Good night, sleep tight, and don't let the bugs bite," he said, and cackled childishly.

"Good night. Thank you."

"Don't worry, there are no bugs at all. Not even bedbugs."

Kinsella locked himself in: he did not know why. Suddenly, he felt tense. The helicopter might be a mistake; it might have been wiser to remain passive, allowing the element of chance, the weather, to lay its onus on the Abbot. Kinsella went into the bathroom and brushed his teeth, then shaved for the second time that day. He stripped and, putting on his one-piece sleeping suit, lay on the narrow bed. With a fanatic like Father Manus, or even that very tall old man, the master of novices, your opposition was in the open, and less dangerous. What *did* the Abbot think? The one argument which seemed to have some effect on him was when he stared at the fire and said, "I didn't think of myself as contradicting Rome. God forbid." Obedience: in the end it was the only card. *Tu es Petrus.* And on this rock I will build my church. And the gates of hell will not prevail against it.

The wind had set up a small rattle in the window frame. Below on the rocky bluff, constant as a ticking clock, the sound of waves, washing on shore. And then, startling as is any human sound in a wild place, Kinsella heard a voice, singing out a hymn.

> "Faith of our fathers living still
> In spite of dungeon fire and sword.
> Oh, how our hearts beat high with joy
> Whene'er we hear that glorious word.
> Faith of our fathers, holy faith,
> We will be true to thee till death,
> We will be true to thee till death."

When the verse ended, he jumped from his bed and ran to the window. No one. Grassy slopes leading to rock-strewn shore. Yet the voice had been close. And now, it began again.

> "Our fathers chained in prisons dark
> Were still in heart and conscience free."

Ran to the front door, unlocked it and went out. The light on the west wall, requested by the Abbot, shone down, casting its beam all along the path and the shore. Where was the singer?

> "How sweet would be our children's fate
> If they, like them, could die for Thee.
> Faith of our fathers, holy faith,
> We will be true to thee till death.
> We will be true to thee till death."

Silence. He stared about him, wind whipping his light zycron sleeping suit, his hair blowing in thick curls about his face. What about the dungeons into which our father's faith put so many poor souls? he wanted to shout. Sing along, you bastard, sing along, it will take more than songs and tricks. I have the power to order, to alter. He went back into the guest house and locked the door. Lay down, reviewing the conversations, the Abbot's remarks, the options. Toward midnight, he set his mind to wake at seven. He turned on his right side. Obedient, his mind admitted sleep.

AT MIDNIGHT, the Abbot left his parlor and went down the winding stairs. He was aware that rules were being broken; certain monks were not in bed. He knew this, without evidence, but as surely as he knew most other details of life on Muck. In time of crisis such things were to be expected. But not permitted. As he went through the sacristy, putting out the lights behind him, he heard a noise in the church. He went in through the door at the south transept.

There were no lights in the church, save a candle before the small shrine to the Virgin, and the red sanctuary lamp over the main altar. In the chancel Father Walter and Father Manus knelt side by side, in semi-darkness, their arms outstretched in that painful posture of adoration which simulates the outstretched arms of the crucified Christ. Behind them, less spectacularly at prayer, were Brothers Sean, John, and Michael, and, sitting on a bench, two of the oldest monks, Father Benedict and Brother Paul. The Abbot's entrance was not noticed, although he made no effort to walk softly. A sign, he knew, that others were expected.

"Father Walter," the Abbot said, in a loud voice.

All eyes sideshot to south transept. All saw the Abbot who saw all. Father Walter, lowering his praying arms, rose stiffly from his knees and marched to the rear of the church to confront his superior. Father Manus was at once joined in cruciform adoration by old Father Benedict.

The Abbot put his arm on Father Walter and drew him out into the night damp of the cloister walk.

"So you are in on this?"

"Have you good news for us, I hope, Tomás?"

"I have no news. I asked you a question."

"Yes. I am the ringleader."

"You are not. Adding a lie to your sins will not help whatever foolish aim you have in mind."

"You know very well what I have in mind. It is what we all have in mind."

"Is it. Do you know *my* mind?"

"Asking God's help is not a sin."

"Breaking the rule of obedience is."

"Tomás, you are not going to be vexed with us, are you?"

"I am very disappointed. I want you to go in there and tell those others to get off to their beds at once."

Father Walter's face went happily into a smile. "Our prayers are answered, so!"

"They are nothing of the sort. There is work to be done in the fields and in the Abbey. The boats will have to be out to the pots and back by noon. The mackerel are running off Slea Head and I want nets out. We live by work, as I have said a hundred times. We are not a contemplative order."

"This is a case when only the power of prayer can help."

"You can not run a monastic community like a holiday camp, Walter. People taking it into their heads to stay up all night without a by-your-leave or with-your-leave. I asked everybody to behave as usual, while this visitor was in the house. I am disappointed in you, Walter."

"It was my fault, so it was, Father Abbot."

"I know who the ringleader is, there is not any sense in you pretending you are he. What you are is my deputy. If I cannot trust you to carry out an order, then where am I?"

"I am sorry, Tomás. I will get them off to bed."

"I do not want to see them ten minutes from now. And I want no holy vigils in cells, do you hear? The holiest thing every man jack of you can do is turn out fit to work in the morning. Good night, now."

"Good night and God bless you," Father Walter said.

The Abbot crossed the cloister to a bay where there was an ambry used for storing wood. He checked the lock which Brother Kevin had reported as broken. It was broken. He heard them in the cloister walk behind him, but did not turn around until all was silence. Then he went back into the church.

A dark church: the flickering oil flame of the sanctuary light over the altar, the gutter of one fat five-day candle beneath the small shrine to Our Lady. The Abbot genuflected, from habit, as he faced the chancel, then sat down heavily on one of the benches near Our Lady's shrine. Looked at the candle, beneath the shrine. Father Donald lit that. Every year, Father Donald's old mother sent him a little money to buy things like warm gloves and mufflers. Every year, he spent it in candles lit, before Our Lady's shrine, in time of trouble. Candles as at Lourdes. "Lourdes is no longer in operation," the Abbot's visitor had said tonight. Lourdes, that sad and dreadful place; the Abbot thought of his own visit to Lourdes, remembering the thousands on thousands of banked candles in the grotto where the Virgin was supposed to have appeared to an illiterate French girl. With four other priests he had arrived on a pilgrimage excursion and, on the first morning, visited the shrine to see the myriad crutches and trusses hung on the grotto wall, the medical bureau with its certifications of "miraculous" cures, the tawdry religious supermarkets, crammed with rosaries and statuettes, the long lines of stretchers and wheelchairs on which lay the desperate and the ill, the stinking waters of the "miraculous" bathing pool. At noon, the Abbot fled to his hotel room, where, pleading dysentery, he shut himself up, seeing no one, until it was time for the excursion train to leave. Two days in that room, trying not to think of what he had seen, trying to say his prayers.

It was not the first time. There had been moments before, sometimes hours, even days, where, back on Muck or in some church on the mainland, that bad time had come on him, that time when, staring at the altar, he knew the hell of the metaphysicians: the hell of those deprived of God. When it came on him, he could not pray; prayers seemed false or without any meaning at all. Then his trembling began, that fear and trembling which was a sort of purgatory presaging the true hell to come, the hell of no feeling, that null, that void. A man wearing the habit of a religious, sitting in a building, staring at a table called an altar on which there is a box called a tabernacle and inside the tabernacle there is a chalice with a lid called a ciborium, and inside the ciborium are twelve round wafers of unleavened bread made by the Sisters of Knock Convent, Knock, Co. Mayo. That is all that is there.

That is all that is in the tabernacle in this building which is said to be the house of God. And the man who sits facing the tabernacle is a man with the apt title of *prelatus nullius,* nobody's prelate, belonging to nobody. Not God's abbot, although sometimes he tries to say the words, "Our Father Who Art in Heaven," but there is no Father in heaven, His name is not hallowed by these words, His kingdom will not come to he who sits and stares at the tabernacle; who, when he tries to pray, enters null; who, when in it, must remain, from day to day, weeks becoming months, and, sometimes, as after Lourdes, a year.

Lourdes was the worst time: it was not the first and it would not be the last. If he prayed. So the Abbot avoided prayer. One could pretend to a preference for private devotions. One's Mass could be said alone. He no longer read his daily office. As for public prayers, in a community like this there were always others, greedy to lead. Sometimes, one had to say a grace. One said the words, but did not pray. If one did not risk invoking God, one did not risk one's peace of mind. He was needed here. He did his work. He did his best. But did not pray. He had not prayed now for, well, he did not want to think. A long time, yes. Some years.

Tonight, he sat in the church, as a man sits in an empty waiting room. After some minutes, footsteps sounded in the nave. The Abbot did not turn around. He, whom he expected, had come.

Father Matthew, six feet five inches tall, the biggest man on Muck, marched up the center aisle of the church with a tread like an armored knight. Master of Novices with no novices to master, an authoritarian figure denied the command he might have graced; in Kilcoole, long ago, he and the Abbot had been seminary classmates, and rivals for the Latin prize. At that time, the world was at war, and Winston Churchill had to deal with a stubborn, righteous, very tall young French general, who led the Free French Forces under the banner of the Cross of Lorraine. Then, as now, physically and in temperament, Father Matthew resembled General de Gaulle. And then, as now, the Abbot knew what Churchill meant when he said "the cross I have to bear is the Cross of Lorraine." Unyielding in his scruples, militant in his devotions, Father Matthew, even in his age, was no man to cross. Now, his hoar-white hair and beard making him a ghost in the near-darkness, he marched toward the altar, his lips moving in muttered devotions.

"Father Matthew!"

Father Matthew stopped, as though brought up short by an invisible fence. His great head probed the shadows. "Ah, Father Abbot. And where are the others?"

"What others?"

"The vigil."

"*What* vigil?"

"It is a vigil of devotion in honor of Our Lady, offered up for the purpose of preserving the Latin Mass on Mount Coom and here on Muck."

"The other monks are in bed. I sent them to bed."

"And why did you do that, Father Abbot?"

"Because I am in charge here."

Father Matthew sighed audibly.

"Father Matthew, it is some years now since I have taken it upon myself to rebuke you. The last thing in the world I want is to reopen our disagreements of former days. There is work to be done tomorrow. You will please go to your bed."

"I have made a solemn promise to Our Lady to hold a vigil in her honor this night."

"When you were ordained as an Albanesian monk, you made a solemn promise to God to obey your superiors. Go to bed."

Father Matthew stood immobile, tall as a round stone tower. "May I ask, then, Father Abbot, what is your decision about Mount Coom?"

From his bench, the Abbot looked up coldly at the tall figure in the aisle. "I am informed by Rome that the Mass is now merely symbolic. Do you understand what I am saying?"

"That is heresy, pure and simple!"

"Why is it heresy, Father Matthew?"

"Because the Mass is the daily miracle of the Catholic faith. The Mass, in which bread and wine are changed by the priest into the body and blood of Jesus Christ. Without that, what is the Church?"

"Then our belief in Jesus Christ and His Church depends on a belief in miracles. Is that it, Matthew?"

"Of course that is it! St. Augustine said, 'I should not be a Christian but for the miracles.' And Pascal said, 'Had it not been for the miracles, there would have been no sin in not believing in Jesus Christ.' Without a miracle, Christ did not rise from His tomb and ascend into heaven. And without that, there would be no Christian Church."

"Our visitor brings an order from our Father General. Would you obey that order, Father Matthew, even if that order instructed you to consider the Mass not as a miracle, but, let's say, just a pious ritual?"

"Far be it from me to speak out against my superiors," Father Matthew thundered, "but I am ashamed to hear that talk coming from you—and under God's roof."

"Are you, now?" the Abbot said, suddenly weary. "But, on the other hand, it seems you are not ashamed to *act* against the orders of your superiors. Even to the point of disobedience."

"I do not consider that I have ever been disobedient to our rule."

"You were told there were to be no vigils or special observances tonight."

"I acted according to my conscience, Father Abbot."

"Did you, indeed? And was it your conscience that sent you down to the shore, a while ago, singing hymns to annoy our visitor?"

"I sang a hymn, yes. Is he the sort of heathen who would be offended by the singing of a Catholic hymn?"

"Hold your tongue!" the Abbot shouted. "Go to your cell. Tomorrow, at suppertime, I want you in front of the chapter with an apology for your behavior. I have had enough of you, Matthew, all these years. Insolence and insubordination is the opposite of every vow you took when you became a monk. Are you not ashamed!"

"Father Abbot, I humbly apologize to you, since you ask me to apologize," Father Matthew said. The Abbot, in twenty years, had never spoken to him in this tone of voice. Shaken, but anxious not to show it, Father Matthew turned and genuflected to the altar. Rising, he made the Sign of the Cross. "Since you order me to retire, I obey your order." Turning, he walked with heavy steps back down the aisle whence he came. The door at the foot of the nave banged shut.

The Abbot sighed. Years ago, he would have knelt and offered up an act of contrition for his unruly temper. But, years ago, he had felt a certainty about so many things. *Aggiornamento,* was that when uncertainty had begun? Changes of Doctrine. Setting oneself up as ultimate authority. Insubordination. He looked at the tabernacle. Insubordination. The beginning of breakdown. And, long ago, that righteous prig at Wittenberg nailing his defiance to the church door.

The Abbot rose. He did not genuflect. He went down the side aisle and out into the night.

3

KINSELLA WOKE at seven. In the rectangle of window above his bed, the sky was already light. Gulls rode that sky, kites held by invisible string. When, dressed and shaven, he opened the guest house door and stepped outside, he met the rush of breakers on shore, a long retreating roar of water. Obbligato of gull cries overhead, their harsh, despairing screams seeming to mourn a death. Winds whipped like penny tops, spinning the long grasses this way and that. The sky, immense, hurried, shifted its scenery of ragged clouds. From the cove below, four curraghs were putting out to sea. A fifth rode, far out, waiting for the others, as, bending to their oars, monks seal-wet in black oilskins pushed the curraghs stiffly over fencelike waves, moving toward the deeps. The day's work had begun. Kinsella turned back toward the land. He felt the loneliness of islands, the sense of being shut in, here on a barren outcropping on the edge of Europe, surrounded by this desolation of ocean. Above him now, on a sloping field, four monks, skirts hitched up, spaded heavy shovels full of black earth. From the monastery itself he smelled the delicate scent of turf fires. An old monk, waiting just inside the cloister entrance, saw Kinsella standing outside the guest house, waved to him, and began to hurry toward him along the muddy path beneath the west wall of the monastery. The monk was not the Abbot of Muck.

Came closer: Father Manus, tall, white-haired, and boyish, with the wanting-to-please smile of the Irish countryside. "Ah, good morning to you, Father. You slept well, I hope?"

"Yes, thank you."

"Father Abbot asked me to find out if you would like to say Mass this morning? It would be easily arranged, so."

Kinsella said he thought not.

"Then we'll put some breakfast into you, will we?"

"The Abbot was supposed to meet me here at eight. Perhaps I should wait?"

"Ah, well, he might be a bit delayed. He told me to look after you. He's trying to get through on the telephone to Galway. We shipped some dulse down there last week and it's still stuck in the railway sheds."

"Dulse?"

"Dried seaweed. It is good eating. They sell it abroad, too. Have you never heard of it?"

"I'm afraid not."

In the refectory, the breakfast plates had already been cleared away. The old kitchen monk put his head around the door. "Two boiled eggs or one?"

"One, thank you."

The second old monk now appeared with a pot of tea and slices of homemade bread.

"Butter, for our visitor. And jam, too," Father Manus said, anxiously.

"I am getting it, so." The old monk sounded cross.

"You see," Father Manus told Kinsella, "we don't eat jam except on special occasions."

"Feast days!" the old monk said, and chortled unexpectedly.

"I will leave you, so, to your breakfast," Father Manus said, withdrawing.

The second old monk approached, bearing a boiled egg on a plate. Kinsella, sensing it was expected, bowed his head and silently said an Ecumen grace. No one said private grace nowadays. Grace was public and used only in mixed Ecumenical groups. The old monk withdrew. The kitchen door shut. Kinsella was alone in the refectory.

It was ten after eight. The Abbot's absence might well be deliberate.

Hartmann, suspended in his back brace, not seeming to be seated, but rather hung in his orthopedic chair, his freckled fingers knitting and unknitting on the outer steerer wheels. "Almost always, the techniques were the same. When the bishops had decided to deny our requests, we were made to wait. Conferences were cancelled, interviews delayed. Excuses offered without conviction. You must show them that while you are the Revolution and they are Tradition, the Revolution is the established faith and will prevail. Power is the concept they have always understood. Use it, and use it from the beginning."

If this monastery was organized as others were, the Abbot would know the exact moment the helicopter was due, might even wait almost to the moment of departure to offer some delaying tactic, or bring a compromise offer into play. It would not do. Immediate compliance could be ordered under threat of transfer. An acting Abbot could be installed at once. There was, however, a complication. The Abbot might not know it, but, under Ecumen Rules, he had the right of appeal to the Amsterdam World Council. He would lose, of course, but the case might drag on for months. And, meantime, he could not be deposed. Such a confrontation was to be avoided. For one thing, it would almost certainly inspire a media circus with the Abbot as martyr. If the Abbot knew these rights of his, Kinsella also knew the catch to them. By Ecumen Rules, the Abbot must, before bringing his case to the Amsterdam World Council, first have had a direct confrontation with his Order Superior. That Superior, Father General Humbertus Von Kleist, of the Albanesian Order, Grand Chancellor of the Pontifical Atheneum of St. Vicente, would face the Abbot on his arrival in Rome. The Abbot would need to be strong. Very strong.

But Kinsella felt it would not come to that. There were ways of shading the options, ways of exploring one's ad-

versary's intentions without actually making a committing
move.

"Was that egg fresh?"

The Abbot had come into the refectory without any
sound. He stood behind his visitor, thumbs hooked in the
broad leather belt in which his rosary was knotted, his face
mild in a morning smile.

"Delicious."

"They are our hens. They were not laying last month,
but they are usually quite cooperative. I hope you slept
well?"

"Yes. And you?"

"I was late to bed," the Abbot said, swinging his leg
over the refectory bench and sitting down opposite Kinsella. At once, as though he had been peering through a
crack in the door, the old kitchen brother appeared. He
set a bowl before the Abbot and poured black tea into it,
then went further down the table, wiping the top off with
a dishcloth. The Abbot looked at the bowl. "Sometimes I
wish my insides were lined with tin, like one of those old
tea chests. I have a terrible taste for tea." He looked
down the long table. "Brother Pius, get back to your work,
if you please!"

"I *am* working," the old brother said, crossly, but
stopped wiping off the table and went back into the
kitchen.

"There is great curiosity," the Abbot said. "The walls
not only have ears, they have tongues as well. They announced to me at first light this morning that a helicopter
is due in here at nine. Is that right?"

"There is supposed to be a bad storm coming up at
noon."

"There is a storm," the Abbot said. "I heard it on the
wireless. It will be here some time today. That is sure.
There will be rain, starting any time now. But that is
nothing new. Rain is what we get most of here, you
know."

Kinsella nodded, hoping to encourage further talk.

"So you are off," the Abbot said.

"I hope so."

"Yes," the Abbot said. "You are right to go. No sense

hanging around. You delivered your letter and that's all that's necessary."

"Not quite all," Kinsella said, very carefully. There was a great silence in the dining hall.

"Brother Pius and Brother Malachy, who is in there with you?" the Abbot shouted, suddenly.

"Nobody at all, Father Abbot."

"Well, get on with your work, then. Let me hear some noise."

There was a sudden rattle of pots and the noise of running water. The Abbot listened to be sure it continued. Then, putting his head to one side in his quizzical fashion, he stared at Kinsella. "Not quite all, you said? Was there something else?"

"You haven't told me what you're going to do. I don't feel I should leave until I know that."

"Do?" the Abbot said. "I will do as I am bid. Father General's letter is perfectly clear. No more Latin Mass here or on Mount Coom. No more private confessions. That is his wish, is it not?"

Kinsella stared; the helicopter on its way now, the Abbot's late arrival, this sudden *volte-face*, this suspicious obedience. What was the trap? he asked himself, even as he nodded, yes, yes, indeed, this was what Father General wanted.

"Then it will be done," the Abbot said. "I had no right to take upon myself decisions which belong to my superiors. I have written a letter of apology to Father General, which I would ask you to deliver for me."

"Yes, of course." What was the catch? There must be a catch.

The Abbot took an envelope from the inner pocket of his robe. "I have not sealed it. You may read it, if you wish."

Carefully, Kinsella put the letter, unread, in the inside pocket of his fatigues jacket. "Why?" he said.

"Why, what? Why read the letter?"

"No. Why have you acted as you did?"

"Because it is my duty to obey."

"Yes, but, earlier, you felt that it was your duty to disobey—to retain the old Mass, and so on."

The Abbot turned and stared at the kitchen door. "They are very nosy," he said. "Let us go outside. You'll want to be getting your bag, won't you?"

"Yes, of course."

Through the cloister they went, and over to the west entrance. Spits of rain in the wind, as the Abbot and his visitor turned onto the muddy path leading to the guest house. The Abbot took Kinsella's arm. "I did not want to discuss it in front of them," he said, distractedly. "You see, that will be the important part, how I break it to them. Some of them are very devout. They will take it hard. No, it will not be easy at all. To tell you the truth I am a bit nervous about it."

"Perhaps you would like me to break it to them."

"Oh, no, no, no," the Abbot said. "I want you to go. I want you away before they know. Oh, believe me, they would bother the life out of you, if they knew what you and I know now."

Bent his head, and gripped his visitor's arm tightly as they faced into the wind. "You asked why I acted as I did. I do not want you to think it was from an excess of zeal. On the contrary, it was, rather, from a lack of it. However, that's neither here nor there, is it? That is of no interest to anyone but me."

"It interests me," Kinsella said.

"I am not a holy man," the Abbot said. "Far from it. I would not like to fly under false colors. There are some holy men here, I suppose. On Muck, I mean. But I am not one of them. I have become a very secular man. Do you know what I mean?"

"I don't think I do."

"I am a sort of foreman here, a sort of manager. It is not a lot different from a secular job. The monks work hard and my job is to keep them together and see that they make a go of it. It's a simple life, here. Little jokes, little triumphs, little disasters. We're like a bunch of children, we pass the days as if we had an endless supply of them. It's only when someone like yourself comes along that we ask ourselves, What are we here for? What good do we do?"

The Abbot stopped outside the guest house door. He

turned the key and pushed the door open. "Ah, you are a tidy man. Bag all packed. You travel light. It is the best way. I'll take your bag."

"No, please."

"Very well, so. Let us go along now to the field. It is nearly nine. I want to get you off, you see, and then I have to face up to it. Face the music. It is all in how you tell them. The thing about being in charge is, you must be firm. As Father General is firm. And yourself. What would you have done if I had said I wouldn't follow orders?"

Kinsella laughed but did not speak.

"You are right, better not ask. By the way, what do you want me to say to the press and the telly people if they call up here?"

"Refer all inquiries to me. James Kinsella, Ecumenical Center Information Office, Amsterdam."

"I will do that," the Abbot said. "Let us cut across this field. Do you see them up there, waiting?"

Ahead, in the field where Kinsella landed yesterday, some ten or fifteen monks were gathered, looking about them, oblivious to the rain, scanning the skies in every direction. "They should be at their work," the Abbot said. "Of course they will all be after me, the minute you go. By the way, if they ask you something, do not answer. Let me deal with them."

As they came up the field, the monks turned to look at them. At that moment, above, the sound of an engine. "Your machine is on the way," the Abbot said, looking up.

"I don't see it."

"I do. It is over there. Here he comes. Right on the dot."

Three monks detached themselves from the larger group. The oldest of them, very tall, with white hair and beard, stood straight in the Abbot's path. "Do you have any news for us, Father Abbot?"

"Are the horses brought up from that lower field to take the load of fertilizer over to Doran's?"

"Yes, they are. May I ask our visitor a question?"

"You may not!" the Abbot said. "Let us pass."

Reluctant, the tall monk drew aside. The Abbot, still

gripping his visitor's arm, hurried him on. "A holy man that," he said. "But a tiresome one."

"You really *are* expecting trouble."

"Not trouble, no. It is just difficult. Ah! There he comes. The frumious bandersnatch."

Engine noise made all speech impossible until the helicopter had landed and throttled back its motor. "You have my letter, have you?"

"Yes, I have."

"Well, safe home to Rome. And good luck to you, Father Kinsella."

"Good luck to you, sir."

The rain was heavy now as the pilot slid open the plexiglass door. Kinsella shook hands with his host, then, bending low, ran to the machine. The pilot reached out to pull him up. The door shut. The monks, in a ragged circle, seemed to press close. But, at that point the helicopter rose, lurched forward, and went out to sea.

Kinsella looked down. The Abbot, standing alone, waved, waved. The other monks bunched in a cluster, stared up at the helicopter as it passed over the Abbey tower, out to that splendour of sea. Kinsella saw the old man, a tiny figure on the promontory of land, turn and walk back toward the monastery gate. The monks, moving as in a pack, followed him in.

HEARD THEIR shuffling feet, their voices, the whisperings as in church in the moment of talk at the end of the silence of a retreat, the mutterings increasing until, although he knew they were not more than twenty monks, they sounded as he imagined a mob might sound: knowing those who were and were not here, knowing that eight fishermen who always had the least to say in community disputes were out now in their curraghs, serving the sea, a master hard as eternity, but the land was a hard master too, yet all the monks from the farm were here, Terence's crew and Daniel's, who worked packing dulse and gathering kelp, yes, there were not more than nine men missing in the whole community, it would be what happened now that would decide it. What I say now. What I say to them now.

"Father Abbot?"

He turned in the cloister, saw all of them crowding in behind the triumvirate: Matthew, Manus, Walter. It was Walter who had called him.

"Yes, Father Walter?"

"Can you tell us, now? The man is gone."

WAITED TILL they were all in, lined up in a long queue in the cloister walk. "Yes, I can tell you, now. Father General, in Rome, has written me a letter of instruction. It will be obeyed. From now on, the new Mass will be said, in English, here and at Cahirciveen. The altars will conform with liturgical changes and will face the congregation. There will be no further private confessions, except in the very special circumstances prescribed, where the nature of the confession warrants private consultation. That is all. We have our orders and it is up to all of us to carry them out to the very best of our ability. I am sure we will do that, won't we?"

He did not look at Matthew, or at Manus, but kept his eyes moving between Father Donald, who had a breakdown last year and was subject to sudden tears, and Brother Kevin, whose hysteria was tight, reined in uncertain check. Something of that nature was what he feared, but the thing to do now was be firm, disperse them, reassert the rule of obedience. "And the first thing we will do," he said, attempting a smile, "is every man jack get back to work. That is all. Now, off you go."

"That is not all!" Father Matthew, angry as Isaiah, pointing an accusatory finger, rearing up in his great height. "Why have you not told the community, Father Abbot, what you told to me last night?"

"Last night I told you to go to bed. Now, I tell you to go to work."

The laughter he had wanted, flickered, then stilled.

"You also told me that we are to consider the Mass, from now on, not as a miracle, but as a 'pious ritual,' I believe you said."

"That is correct."

"How can a thing be a miracle one day and not a miracle the next day?"

"Maybe you are a greater theologian than the Pope or

the Vatican Council, Father Matthew. I am not. I am a monk and I do as I am bid."

"No, no, no, no!" As the Abbot had feared, Father Donald had come to tears. "That is sacrilege, that is blasphemy. No, no, no, I can't be hearing that, no, no!"

The Abbot put his arm comfortingly on Father Donald's shoulders. "Now, Donald," the Abbot said. "You are not yourself, you mustn't be getting excited like this. Come along, everybody. Let's get to work."

"And *I* will not be put off like that," Father Matthew shouted. "I will not be ordered to believe something which I do not believe."

"No one can order belief," the Abbot said. "It is a gift from God." But even as he said this, said the only truth left to him, he saw in these faces that he was failing, that he was losing them, that he must do something he had never done, give something he had never given in these, his years as their abbot. What had kept him in fear since Lourdes must now be faced. What he feared most to do must be done. And if, in doing it, I enter null and never return, amen. My time has come.

Matthew, bent on trouble, began again. "You can all see what is being proposed here. It is a denial of everything the Mass stands for."

The Abbot held up his hands, commanding silence. There was silence. He turned and held open the door which led into the nave. "Please. Let us go into the church."

Stood, holding the door for them, as they moved past him, his eyes on their faces, these faces he knew better than his own, seeing every shade of wavering, from confusion, to doubt, to anger at him, to fear, to Father Donald's dangerous tears and Brother Kevin's hysterics, tight on snaffle, a horse ready to bolt. He entered behind them and shut the door. Moved past them in the aisle, going up into the great vault of the nave, moving in that silence, in the gray light of this place where he had spent the longest years of his life, this place where his body would lie, this place he feared most. He entered the chancel. He faced the altar.

"A miracle," he told them, "is when God is there in the tabernacle."

"But you said the opposite, you said that the sacrifice of the Mass is just ritual, that bread and wine remain bread and wine, that there are no miracles!"

Matthew, thundering: righteous, wronged. The Abbot, his back to all of them, heard their stiff intake of breath, the fear of their lives at these words, said in this place. He stared at the golden door of the tabernacle. His fear came. "Prayer is the only miracle," he said. "We pray. If our words become prayer, God will come."

Slowly, with the painful stiffness of age, he went down heavily on one knee, then on both. Knelt in the center of the aisle, facing the altar, the soles of his heavy farm boots showing from the hem of his robe. He trembled. He shut his eyes. "Let us pray."

He bent his head. "Our Father, Who art in Heaven," he said. His trembling increased. He entered null. He would never come back. In null.

He heard them kneel. "Our Father, Who art in Heaven." Relieved, their voices echoed his.

"Hallowed be Thy name," the Abbot said.

"Hallowed be Thy name."

Angel of Beachhouses and Picnics

Anne Sexton

ANGEL of beachhouses and picnics do you know soli-
taire?
Fifty-two reds and blacks and only myself to blame.
My blood buzzes like a hornet's nest. I sit in a kitchen chair
at a table set for one. The silverware is the same
and the glass and the sugar bowl. I hear my lungs fill and
expel
as in an operation. But I have no one left to tell.

Once I was a couple. I was my own king and queen
with cheese and bread and rosé on the rocks of Rockport.
Once I sunbathed in the buff, all brown and lean
watching the toy sloops go by, holding court
for busloads of tourists. Once I called breakfast the sexiest
meal of the day. Once I invited arrest

at the peace march in Washington. Once I was young and
bold
and left hundreds of unmatched people out in the cold.

Angel of Blizzards and Blackouts

Anne Sexton

Angel of blizzards and blackouts, do you know rasp-
  berries,
those rubies that sat in the green of my grandfather's
  garden?
You of the snow tires, you of the sugary wings, you freeze
me out. Let me crawl through the patch. Let me be ten.
Let me pick those sweet kisses, thief that I was
as the sea on my left slapped its applause.

Only my grandfather was allowed there. Or the maid
who came with a scullery pan to pick for breakfast.
She of the rolls that floated in the air, she of the inlaid
woodwork all greasy with lemon, she of the feather and
  dust,
not I. None the less I came sneaking across the salt lawn
in barefeet and jumping-jack pajamas in the spongy dawn.

Oh Angel of the blizzard and blackout, Madam white face,
take me back to that red mouth, that July 21st place.

Drinking Smoke

(AN ABBREVIATED AUTOBIOGRAPHY)

B. H. Friedman

> The two Christians met many people, men
> and women, who were going to their villages,
> with a firebrand in the hand and herbs to
> drink the smoke thereof, as they are accus-
> tomed.
> —Tuesday, Nov. 6, 1492,
> *The Journal of Christopher Columbus*

Even as a small boy I want to smoke. Cigars, at first.
They are what men smoke: fat, dark brown Havanas.

In the den the air becomes dense and dizzying. Beneath
this mantle of gray clouds my father, my maternal grandfather, and my uncles play auction bridge. They light and
relight their cigars, chewing them short at one end as they
burn short at the other. They puff blue-gray smoke into the
air. One uncle purses his lips and blows rings; I watch
in awe as they move up from the card table, lose their
distinct shape, and become lost among the dark clouds.

If I show no expression and make no comment, I am
permitted to stand behind my father and peek over his
shoulder as he arranges his cards, bids, plays his hand.
The tip of his cigar is about a foot from my face or perhaps
for a moment it rests, almost as close, in an ashtray at
the corner of the table. Either way the smoke drifts into
my eyes and nose and mouth, where I feel its sharp
masculine bite. However, I remain as expressionless and
silent as the cards being played.

I am not taught how to play cards or how to smoke.
These things happen naturally. They are absorbed.

Sometimes Father tells me that my standing behind him
brings him luck. This makes me happy. So does his letting
me empty ashtrays. The butts and ashes swirl darkly in
the toilet bowl.

When the game is over and the men have rejoined the women in the living room, my mother excuses herself to open the windows in the den. She complains that the odor of tobacco gets into the upholstery, the carpet, the walls themselves. She says that this odor is unclean. Intuitively I understand that it lurks at the very core of the men's world of games and sports and business. I have seen grand slams go up in smoke. Later I will see athletic championships and big business deals go the same way. I will watch smoke pour from my father's mouth as if his mind is on fire. And I will watch also as cigars die in the crushing embrace of his jaws.

In the living room Grandfather sinks into the deepest, most comfortable chair, relaxing with his final cigar of the evening. He turns it slowly as he smokes so that it will burn evenly and the ash will not droop. This is another game—seeing how long an ash he can produce without dropping it—a game he could not play while playing cards. Though seventy, his hands are steady. They support the family.

Until he dies, my mother does not smoke. Then, in grief, she begins. She smokes constantly, as if trying to catch up on all the smoking the men have done. She brings to smoking a new quality, that of elegance. At first she smokes Marlboros with what is called an ivory tip. Then she switches to a red tip so that her lipstick will not show. Ordinary packs of twenty will not last a day. She buys flat or cylindrical tins of fifty. From these she fills a thin gold case with a sapphire-studded clasp. As her consumption increases she begins to use a cigarette holder. It becomes part of her, alternately part of her hand and part of her face. She smokes nervously, in quick puffs, but gently, without aggression. There is no biting or chewing. As previously I got Father's cigar boxes, I now get Mother's tins to fill with marbles, chestnuts, matchbook covers, the things I collect.

So far I smoke only through my parents' mouths and nostrils, but by the time I finish grade school I try two or three of Mother's cigarettes. I puff them in front of the bathroom mirror, getting the smoke in and out of my mouth as quickly as possible. I attempt to blow it out through my nose as if inhaling. Inhaling itself makes me cough and feel dizzy. Nevertheless, I like what I see in the mirror: a little movie star, perhaps a Dead End Kid, tough and with a lot of savvy. Inevitably, I steal one of the expensive cigars from Father's humidor. (Taking Mother's cigarettes did not seem at all like stealing.) I bite off the tip, the way I have seen him do it, and spit the end into the toilet. I try to light the cigar. This is work, not like lighting a cigarette. I use several matches, circling the end of the cigar as he does to get an even light. The smoke is as strong as steel. I cough, wondering how he can smoke this powerful thing, he and the others— Grandfather, my uncles, movie gamblers, bankers, cab drivers, businessmen in general. I feel more guilty about wasting the cigar, flushing most of it down the toilet, than I do about stealing it.

Several times at high school I smoke cigarettes given to me by classmates. By now I can blow the smoke out through my nose to give the impression I am inhaling, but real inhaling still makes me cough and feel dizzy. Finally I buy my first pack of cigarettes. I go to a wedge-shaped tobacco shop at Columbus Circle on the fringe of the first-run movie theater district. The store has cigarettes of all nations. I select Sweet Caporals, which are no longer popular, but which I remember as the brand Studs Lonigan "pasted in his mug." I can hardly wait to get out of the store and smoke one. Walking down Broadway with the cigarette lit, I feel both manly and elegant. I feel as sophisticated as Adolphe Menjou or William Powell. A beggar asks me if I can spare a smoke. I give him a cigarette. Nobody has ever asked me for one before.

Weeks later I still have five or six cigarettes left. Mother finds the crumpled pack in the pocket of my reversible. She cries. How could I do this to myself? To my health? To her? To Father? She takes the cigarettes one by one, crushes them, and flushes them down the toilet. I am told to stay in my room until Father gets home from work. I fear the worst—a beating and a cut in my allowance. I cannot concentrate on homework. The geometry problems are blurred through the film of Mother's tears.

Father arrives. Through the bedroom door I hear

Mother's voice, then his. He says something about all boys smoking. There is, I think, an element of pride as well as annoyance in his voice. The annoyance may be because this is when he usually reads his evening paper. Their conversation continues, but I cannot make out the words.

Father enters my room. In one hand he holds the newspaper, in the other a cigar. He puts the cigar in his mouth so that he can slam the door. This he does decisively but not angrily. The noise from the door and then the silence which follows emphasize our isolation: this talk will be man-to-man, Mother might as well be miles away. He puffs on his cigar. I wait.

"Your mother tells me you've been smoking?"

"Yes."

"How long?"

"A few weeks."

"Never before?"

"Once or twice."

Father studies me, looking for the slightest hint of deception, a shift in my eyes, a tremor, or perhaps some symptom already signifying the habitual use of tobacco. My heart pounds. I wonder if he can hear it admitting the terrible thing I have done.

"Smoking is a stupid habit—stupid and expensive and unhealthy. It's like burning up money, burning up your lungs. I wish I'd never begun." He pauses, then says, "I wish I could stop." This is difficult for him to say, difficult for me to hear. It has not occurred to me that there is anything he cannot do. "I began, just like you, by having an occasional cigarette. Pretty soon I was smoking them all the time. And the cigar after dinner became the cigar after breakfast. I don't want you to get into that. Make me a promise—"

Again he pauses, rests his cigar on my night table, and waits now for the promise. I know, of course, what it must be, but even so I am reluctant, as if with a school friend, to promise in advance. The promise must first be stated.

"What?" I ask.

"That you won't smoke until you're twenty-one. By then I hope you'll have sense enough not to want to."

It is not a difficult promise. Except for making me feel

older, closer to my parents, cigarettes mean nothing to me. *Except—*

"I promise," I say, feeling suddenly that I have done nothing bad and maybe even something good. I certainly don't feel that I have been punished.

As if to confirm this, Father says, "If you keep your word, I will give you a car when you are twenty-one." This he had intended to use, if necessary, to extract my promise. Now he just gives it to me for being good. He adds, "The car won't even cost anything. You'll save that much by not smoking."

He is smiling as he leaves my room. He has "sold" me and is anxious to tell Mother the good news. In his excitement he leaves the cigar on my night table.

I BREAK MY PROMISE soon after enlisting in the navy, just before my eighteenth birthday.

Boot camp is an introduction to smoking. There, between classes and before mustering for meals, we are permitted time for a smoke. Just that and no more. There is no time for anything else. If one doesn't smoke, the time is wasted. I accept a cigarette from one buddy or another. It would be unfriendly not to. The cigarettes are a way of establishing contact. Soon I begin to carry them, if only to reciprocate. After ten weeks of boot camp I find that a pack lasts me easily two days. On leave, before being assigned to a ship, I have no trouble doing without cigarettes. This way there's less chance that Father will ask about smoking. However, I have decided that if he does ask, I will tell him. I am certain he will consider the war an extenuating circumstance and understand how far away the age of twenty-one must seem to me. No doubt he, too, wonders if I will ever reach that age.

Aboard ship, in the Pacific, I really learn to smoke. There is so much time. The navy does what it can to fill it. I chip paint that is almost fresh, hammering away at the nonexistent corrosion. I wire-brush. I cover the raw steel with red lead and then gray deck paint. Slowly I work my way from bow to stern. When I finish I start over again. The ship is seemingly as endless as an oval track, as endless as the Pacific itself, as endless as the war.

Always in one hand there is a hammer or a brush, in the other a cigarette. Smoking, like chipping paint, is a way of measuring time by waste. In an hourglass the sand is used over and over again; the time returns. But the pieces of tobacco in a cigarette are literally wasted, used up, disposed of; the time is really gone, it will never return.

Four hours on, eight off I stand watch. Whether in the wheelhouse or at a gun station, I am allowed ten minutes in each hour for coffee and a cigarette. For fifty minutes I think about that cigarette. Nothing else seems as important. Not the zigzag course we are steering. Not the kamikaze pilots who may be hidden in the sky. Not the full load of ammunition we are carrying for the invasion of Japan. The stars themselves are unimportant, they cannot light my cigarette. After fifty minutes I move as quickly as possible from the blacked-out wheelhouse or gun station, down a ladder and across the dark deck, to the hatch leading to the galley. I part the heavy curtains and light up. For the remaining minutes I smoke. Just that. Everything else is details: the coffee, the words spoken.

Cigarettes cost five cents a pack. I smoke through half a dozen brands—all that are available in the ship's store— until I find Camels, my brand, heavier, more Turkish than the others. Soon I don't even have to tell the storekeeper what I want. It's enough to say I want a carton.

I love Camels. Neither with family nor friends have I ever had a relationship such as the one I have now with this cigarette, a relationship so intimate, so steady, so dependable. The Camels are always there, over my heart in the pocket of my denim shirt, asking nothing, ready to give what I want, ready to die for me. I do not yet know that I am ready to die for them, that I would sacrifice myself, my family, my friends, my country for a cigarette. I do not know that the relationship is perfect in its reciprocity.

Not only do I love the Camels themselves, I love their package, more than the American flag, more than any masterpiece of ancient or modern art. No picture means as much to me as this one of a camel placed squarely on the sand in front of pyramids and palms. How calm he is, how unruffleable. How proud, with his nose high in the dry desert air. How timeless: he may give time to others, he is beyond it himself. What a perfect pet he is. Again, it will take years before I know that I am his pet too.

Though Camels are loyal to me, I betray them. I try cigars. White Owls, Phillies—these are what the older men aboard ship smoke, the men in their early twenties with stripes on their sleeves and tattoos on their arms, the guys who are making a career of the navy or those who have learned some skill before coming in. Like them, sometimes I smoke a cigar while playing poker. The cigars do not taste or smell like those my father and my uncles smoked, but chewing on them is satisfying: I chew time, I attack it from both ends.

Though cigarettes are very cheap and we all receive about the same pay, toward the end of the month there are those with money and those without; some are always broke. They have lost their money at poker or spent it all in some port; perhaps having spent everything, they traded their cigarettes for whiskey or sex. Gladly we offer ours as Pop, aged 26, the oldest enlisted man in the crew, delivers his basic lecture on Darwinian capitalism:

"If all the money in the world were divided equally between all the people in the world, it would take about six months for those who had money to have it again and for those who had nothing to have nothing."

"Right."

"You are so right."

"That's the way it is."

Heads nod in agreement. Those who have bummed cigarettes smoke silently.

Little Willy, a heavy smoker who sleeps in the bunk below mine, says nothing. He has no money and no cigarettes, but he neither nods his agreement nor smokes. He will not smoke again until he receives his pay. He sits with his lips pressed tightly together, knowing that he still has six days to go. Like me, he smokes Camels. Several times I offer him mine, and I leave the pack on the table while we play cards. He does not mind borrowing money and returns it on payday, but he is determined to sweat out not smoking till then. By now smoking is, of course, part of my life, perhaps the best part. That Little Willy, this

small man with such great pride, can stop, even tem-
porarily, is awesome. I wonder if, when all the money is
divided between all the people, Willy won't come out
all right. He can exist on nothing but what's in him. He
has long sideburns, twenty or more years before they
again become fashionable. They, too, come out of him.
His is another lecture on capitalism, but it is silent, as
silent as smoking or growing hair. Without words he says
one can exist on nothing.

THE WAR ENDS in a cloud of smoke. We dump our load of
ammunition outside Yokohama. We pick up troops and
take them to Guam. From there we proceed to Manila for
orders. There is constant scuttlebutt that we will go home,
but for nine more months we drift. We are sent to Min-
danao, where thousands of natives wait to be returned to
their homes on the other side of the island. It took them
two years through jungles and over mountains to escape
the Japanese. Our LST makes the trip in a week, one
trip after another after another. There seems to be no end
to the natives filing out of the jungle and waiting for us on
the beach. Cigarettes are a greater part of our lives than
ever. We smoke them constantly; we trade them for
bananas, coconuts, souvenirs, women. Cigarettes are time
and time is money.

Finally the job is done. Almost a year after the war has
ended, it ends for us. I return home with a Japanese saber,
a Mindanaoan kris, and a case of Camels (24 cartons,
4800 cigarettes). My parents are appreciative. Cigarettes
are still scarce. We spend my first night home smoking
together. I have just become twenty-one, so it's all right.

Gently Father asks, "What are you going to do?"

"In the fall I'd like to return to college."

My parents are pleased. I am the same boy they sent
off to war. However, they have read many articles on the
returning veteran, they don't push. For some time we
continue to smoke before Father asks, "And this summer?"

"I don't know."

"You can't just sit around smoking," he says despite
himself, despite all the articles.

Mother glares at him. I excuse myself and go to my

room. I can hear their voices rise. "See?" Mother is saying, "You should have waited. He just got home."

By the following day I have decided on what I want to do that summer. I want to sit around and smoke. I no longer know any other life.

I begin to read again. I read about other people in other worlds doing other things besides smoking. But while I read I smoke.

This continues at college. There I learn also to drink. In the navy there wasn't much opportunity, only occasional nights in port. Now I can drink every night, as much as I want, as long as I want. I had not realized how well smoking and drinking go together. Nicotine and alcohol complement each other like two children at the ends of a seesaw. I watch them—aspects of me—go up and down.

By the end of senior year my education seems complete. I am ready to enter business. I have even found a girl who likes smoking and drinking as much as I do. We both smoke Camels. We are meant for each other. Together we climb on the seesaw.

However, my education—ours now—continues. We receive many wedding gifts, most meant to last, but the best is transient, a small jar of Yucatan Purple. We have smoked marijuana a few times at college and at jazz clubs, but not of this quality. Our friend has cleaned it with great care. It is regal in appearance and effect. Up, up we go, past the haze of alcohol, past the highest cloud of tobacco smoke, until we can barely see our bodies down there, laughable little creatures, clutching their Camels and cocktails, always wanting something else. There is nothing we want, nothing to do, and so much time to do it in.

It will take years in business to understand why this drug, as opposed to nicotine and alcohol, is illegal. Yet the reason is simple. Marijuana is subversive. It kills time, bends it, warps it. It makes a mockery of clocks, schedules, programs. Is it any wonder that the political/judicial/economic/technological/etc. system we call the government is opposed to it? Marijuana itself is opposed to the entire system, incompatible with it.

So in business I use the socially acceptable drugs. I

smoke from nine to five, five days a week. There is always a carton of Camels in my desk. Seeing to that is one of my secretary's jobs. And I learn to handle first one, then two, martinis at lunch. I learn to smoke more in the afternoon to counteract the martinis. I smile through the day. There is always something good going on inside my lungs or my stomach.

Outside me it is much like the navy. Business, too, has its standing watch and chipping paint, its necessary and unnecessary work. But now my real job is to make decisions, something I never had to do in the navy. Each week, for at least two hours out of forty, I make decisions. During the other thirty-eight I chip paint. The trouble is I never know when the two hours will come, what arbitrary pattern of minutes they will fall into. So I must be there all forty hours. I must stand watch. At least I can smoke any time, and I do, all the time. I smoke when I'm reading my mail. I smoke when I'm on the phone. I smoke when I'm dictating. I smoke when I'm negotiating contracts. I smoke when I'm making decisions. The decision to smoke is the first step toward the next decision.

The years burn by. The size of my office grows. The size of my paycheck grows. The size of my family grows. Friends tell me it is remarkable that I haven't gained weight. I give the credit to cigarettes, just as I do when they notice that I am still smiling when a deal breaks up. I have something to smile about, that carton of Camels in my desk. However, cigarettes are not a guarantee of good health. The days begin with coughing. My wife and I cough good morning to each other. Often I feel a sharp pain in my chest. Sometimes my hands and feet are cold. My breath is short.

In the early fifties, as evidence comes out connecting smoking with lung cancer and other awful diseases, my wife tries several times to stop. She walks around the apartment with a simulated cigarette in her mouth, taking it out only to snap at the children or me. At dinner parties she delivers lectures on the suicidal aspects of smoking. She allows no one to smoke in peace. But soon she herself is smoking again, if unpeacefully. She deserts Camels, tries the new Kents, struggles to get enough smoke into her lungs to satisfy her. Then she switches to a Dunhill holder and takes pride in showing everyone how dark and dirty the crystal filter becomes.

We take a trip to Paris. Her packing is mostly Dunhill filters. Mine is Camels. Mornings, while she prepares her costume, makeup, and smoking equipment, I get in the habit of waiting for her at a small cafe near the hotel. There I read the *Tribune*. One day, as the minutes become hours, I run out of Camels and buy Gauloises. They are a revelation, another step toward Turkey, another step toward Truth. I study the winged helmet on the blue pack, a flying faceless head. The helmet is not as pretty as the camel, but by the time my wife joins me at the cafe table I have switched. Camels no longer give me what I want. Gauloises become my Yucatan Purple. Or they are cigars disguised as cigarettes. I can see those Turks—like those Cubans, or Mexicans, or whatever from far away—slapping their thighs in the fields. I feel the rhythm. My heart marches to a different drummer.

On the way home we spend a few days in Madrid. In a drugstore there I buy Asthmaticos, intended for asthmatic smokers. These cigarettes are supposed to be made with hemp. I approach them as if they are another leg of my Journey to the East, a Moorish side-trip perhaps. I light one, inhale deeply, feel nothing but a rasping in my throat as the burning cigarette crackles drily. They taste so bad I can't get through a pack, not even with my wife's help. At a restaurant I leave the remaining Asthmaticos along with the waiter's tip. He smiles knowingly.

Like Sweet Caporals, like the brands I tried in the navy before finding Camels, Asthmaticos are a brief affair. Camels I had been married to for some twenty years. Though we are divorced, the relationship lingers, especially when I can't get Gauloises. It takes time to know my new bride. She leaves a different taste in my mouth, a different smell in the room. Gauloises are the most public cigarette. They wear the largest wedding ring. They insist that they have been there, wherever there is.

When I return from Europe, *there* is right in my desk. For a while I might as well be smoking marijuana. Everyone in the office wants to know what I am doing, what I am trying to prove. They smell a foreign smell. I offer Gauloises to those who are interested. They smoke, cough, and never ask again. Now I am not only the thin smiling executive but the one with lungs of steel.

THE SURGEON GENERAL's report is published. The number of brands and types of cigarettes proliferates. There are new names, new filters, new sizes. My wife tries them all. I remain faithful to Gauloises, *sans filtre*.

My son begins to smoke. I find myself saying some of the same things to him that my father said to me, and I say them with a cigarette in my mouth. For the first time, I wish that, as an example to my son, I could stop smoking. I even do some of the same kind of arithmetic Father did. I figure that for twenty-five years I have smoked an average of two packs a day, 365,000 cigarettes, at a cost of about 40¢ a pack, or a total of almost $15,000, not counting cigars or more exotic smokes.

The arithmetic doesn't impress my son. I notice that in the summer when we take a walk on the beach he, like me, must now tuck cigarettes and matches into the waistband of his bathing suit. I am envious of the children who run freely, without props.

My son and I used to play a game. We would swim to a point about fifty yards offshore and then see how far back we could swim underwater without coming up for air. For several years he gained on me, then passed me, but now, after about twenty yards we both come up panting for air.

I must make a four-day business trip. It annoys me, as does having to carry cigarettes on the beach, that for this trip, I must carry a carton of Gauloises, knowing that I probably won't be able to get them where I'm going and without even being certain that they will last four days. I decide that I will try to make it without them and mention this to a friend who has stopped smoking.

"No," he says, "you must take them with you. You must know you have them if you want them. Otherwise you'll be bumming cigarettes from everyone else or buying whatever's available. Whenever you want a cigarette, just tell yourself that you just finished one. I still do that after almost two years."

I am surprised that he still thinks about cigarettes. I believe that if I can stop for four days I can stop forever.

In the plane I drink more than usual. I look at several magazines, hardly able to concentrate on the words. My vocabulary is limited: the only noun I know is cigarette, the only verb is smoke. I flip past the ads for cigarettes, telling myself that I have just had one. I try not to think about the passengers who are smoking. I try not to think about the carton of Gauloises in my suitcase. I welcome the NO SMOKING sign when it is on. Then I can tell myself that I wouldn't be smoking anyway. I don't like telling myself that I have just had one. I don't believe it. My last cigarette seems ages ago.

With the help of many drinks I get through the first day. I fall asleep wondering, if I had to play some silly willful game, if I would not have been better off giving up alcohol. The sections of my liver that I see in my mind look at least as diseased as those of my lungs.

The next morning is the first in many, many years that I have not started with a cigarette. I reach toward the night table and the Gauloises are not there. They are still in my suitcase. I wonder if I will be able to get out of bed, shave, have breakfast, get to my meeting, get through the day, do all these things without cigarettes. I move sluggishly, as if some switch that is usually turned on in the morning has been left off. Before leaving the hotel room I put a pack of cigarettes in my pocket just in case.

Just in case what? Just in case the craving continues? Of course it does. It intensifies. At the meeting my mind wanders constantly to my pocket. I touch the lump there, appreciating the relief it contains but resenting it too, this small blue package weighing less than two ounces, which grows larger and larger, heavier and heavier. Even before noon I suggest that we recess for lunch, by which I mean a drink.

The drink helps. So does the second and the third. So does the food. Everything helps that goes in my mouth. I am starving. I am gasping for smoke, for fuel. I would like to go on eating and drinking forever. Without cigarettes there is no punctuation to the meal, no clear ending; it runs on.

We return to the meeting. I try not to bicker over small matters. There is only one small matter worth bickering about, that pack of cigarettes in my pocket. My mind and my body are in constant dialogue. My body says it has become accustomed to nicotine. It pleads. My mind refuses. Other items being discussed at the conference table are unimportant, a background buzz of meaningless words. I wonder if I am any longer of use to my company. I wonder if it wouldn't be honorable to resign. I feel useless, weak, vulnerable, so vulnerable. I am like that classic dream-figure who is naked when everyone else wears clothes. I wear nothing, not even a screen of smoke.

After the meeting I have another drink and call home. I think that I want to find out how my family is. I discover that I want to tell them how I am. I want to tell them about my mouth, my nose, my lungs, my nerves. My wife and children are not particularly interested. They have their own lives, the house, the car, school.

I do not remember having dreamed about smoking the previous night, but tonight that's all I dream about. Cigarettes march through my mind as if in TV commercials. I smoke many of them. I awaken feeling as if all night I have done nothing but smoke. I can hardly believe that the one pack of cigarettes is still unopened in my jacket and that the rest of the carton is in my suitcase. Now I can tell myself that I have just had a cigarette, dozens, while I slept.

Each day not smoking becomes a little easier, not much but a little. I smoke only in my sleep. During the day I continue to eat and drink more and more. To avoid alcohol I drink water. I go frequently to the fountain, then to the men's room. I wonder if anyone notices this. I wonder if they notice that I am not smiling as much.

My sense of taste begins to change. It is not that food tastes better, as I have been told it would, but that I have a great desire for sweets. Suddenly I want candy, chewing gum, desserts. Instead of scotch I want bourbon. Martinis taste as good as ever, or maybe they do taste better.

When I return home, I look differently at my wife. I

want to taste her, I want to smoke her, every orifice, beginning with her ears and nostrils and working down. I want to smoke every pore in her body. I want to smoke her toes. . . . I look differently at all women. I have fantasies about blindfold tests. Every woman says TASTE ME.

Perhaps if once (a week ago) cigarettes controlled me, I am now out of control. At the office I try not to show my irritability. At home I let loose. I shout about too much salt or too little, a picture or a piece of furniture being out of place, anything. My son says giving up smoking is not worth this. My daughter says she wishes I would smoke again. No doubt my wife wishes that too, but tactfully she says only that I've changed.

"How?" I demand.

"You're more—more impossible than before."

I go on dreaming about smoking. In one dream I am at a store where there are no Gauloises available. I ask for Camels. There are none of those either. Lucky Strikes? Chesterfields? Old Golds? Pall Malls? Picayunes? Sweet Caporals? Nothing. In desperation I ask for Asthmaticos. Not even those. This night I eat candy. In other dreams I get my cigarettes and wake up in the morning with my chest burning.

I gain weight. At first my clothes feel tight. They remind me that I should eat and drink less. But now I must have suits let out, I must learn to accept the new pounds which are part of me. Soon no material remains to be let out. I buy new suits, shirts with larger collars. I explain to my wife that I am doing all this with the money saved by not smoking. In some ways I feel more guilty about not smoking than I ever felt about smoking. Often now I feel the need to explain. I explain to my wife that I don't mind her smoking, that she shouldn't mind my not smoking, that I don't feel superior to her or to others who smoke, that I'm able again to enjoy watching others smoke, that much of this pleasure is visual, etc., etc., etc. My wife says I sound like a broken record. A broken track record, I think. I am really quite proud of myself. By now I haven't smoked for over a month.

I have a more mysterious dream. In it I go to the Museum of Modern Art and then nearby for a long lunch with several martinis and lots of cigarettes. After lunch I walk along the street looking for the museum, to which I want to return. I see only an excavation. As I look down into the hole a girl says, "I loved your show." I assume she means the excavation. Before I can say anything, she adds, "Especially that big fire hydrant." I want to tell her I'm not Oldenburg. But again she speaks: "And now I can't find the museum. It was just here a few hours ago."

"I know, I'm looking for it too. Things happen fast in New York. Maybe the museum was relocated. Maybe they moved it across the street."

We cross Fifty-third, looking for the museum. We rush up and down the block and around the corner. We are still searching when I awaken. Again there is the burning in my lungs from the fires which won't go out, fires begging for fuel. . . . The dots indicate a continuation, a continuing desire for cigarettes. But what does the dream mean? Anxiously I grind my teeth. Perhaps I need medical help.

It happens I have my quarter-annual appointment with the periodontist. For years he has told me that if I cut down on smoking, my teeth and gums will be in better shape. Now I am not so sure. The heat and nicotine may be harmful, but so is the acid which builds up from the tension of not smoking. I wonder to what extent one's health is dependent on external factors. Just as the best athletes break the most bones and strain the most muscles (including the heart), and just as the best swimmers drown, the body takes its revenge on our efforts to lead a so-called healthy life.

I look around the waiting room. Almost everyone is smoking. It is a way to deal with waiting. The smoke moves up sinuously from the magazines. It is alive. Smoking has begun to *look* attractive. Here and in movies revived on TV and in restaurants and bars, the attractive, high-strung people, those who look as if they have something to smoke *about*, all seem to be smoking. It is the most elegant tic. I don't feel elegant. Once again I am the only naked person in the room. I sit, heavy in my chair, thinking how much the cigarette companies must love to see thirties' movies revived, with all that carefree smoking in the days before talk of a relationship to cancer—or even periodontal problems. Are the stars all dead, they and their particular styles of smoking? Valentino, Stroheim, Bogart, Powell, Menjou—in my mind I am listing them and watching them smoke when the nurse announces that the doctor will see me.

He clucks his tongue, signifying that my mouth is in bad shape. "You'd better see me again in two months rather than three. What have you been doing?"

"I've been not smoking."

He smiles, waits. "And?"

"I'm eating more. Especially sweets. And I'm drinking more. Sweet drinks. Bourbon rather than scotch."

"Very common among alcoholics—"

He leaves me with that thought, suspended in the air along with the drill and other dental equipment, as he places the mask over my nose and feeds me nitrous oxide. For a moment I fight the gas, wanting to formulate a reply. Dentists aren't really doctors, I think—they're doctors who couldn't get into medical school—and doctors aren't psychiatrists, and psychiatrists don't know much about alcoholism anyway.

The dentist scrapes the roots of my teeth. My thoughts move along with the steady flow of laughing gas. I wonder if tartar formation, tooth decay, gum damage, and the rest couldn't be detected just as they begin and the conditions be corrected before they become serious. Perhaps quarterly checkups, even bi-monthly, aren't enough. Perhaps I should see the dentist every month, every week, every day. Yes, every day at some appointed moment my teeth should be checked, cavities nipped in the bud. Yes, yes, yes . . . thirty-two times yes. So much for the teeth. The rest of the machinery must be checked too: the eyes, the heart, the mind . . . I see myself spending a large part of the day—at least the entire morning—preparing for my trips out into the other world, the one outside my own body. My life will be like that of an airplane: checkups, maintenance, refuelings, flights. We deserve the same attention as expensive machines. . . .

The gas is turned off, the mask removed. I rinse. Half an hour has passed. I have forgotten what the dentist said about alcoholics. I don't want a drink. I want more gas.

I wish it flowed through me all the time as nicotine once did. I want to feel good.

It is strange that, though I didn't think much about my health when I was smoking, just as I didn't think much about smoking when I was smoking, I think about both so much now. In this I am not alone. The newspapers are full of stories about health: new drugs, new operations, new statistics. I seek more traditional medical wisdom. I love articles on acupuncture. I love this, from an interview with Alice Roosevelt Longworth: ". . . nothing to say on that subject [sex] except, if one wishes to talk about bodily functions, fill what's empty, empty what's full, and scratch where it itches."

THE EMBERS will not die. They still burn in my lungs, though I try to drown them in alcohol. I have refused marijuana because I do not want to be that directly reminded of smoking. A friend who has given up smoking assures me that they are not the same thing, that there is no risk. I accept the joint that is passed to me. How good it feels to place this skinny cigarette between my lips, to suck in the smoke, to hold it in my lungs. My friend is right. Marijuana is different from tobacco. It is gentler, less demanding, less insistent. One doesn't always want more. One is content.

Occasionally now I smoke marijuana. It is soothing and as full of chuckles as nitrous oxide. It is the laughing leaf. My wife marvels. She says I am becoming easier to live with. I am determined to make her marvel more. To celebrate the first anniversary of not smoking, I produce a cigar and light it after dinner. My lungs catch on fire. My head whirls. Alas, I cannot smoke without inhaling. I feel so dizzy I put out the cigar. I also feel stupid. However, a few weeks later, when I am high on alcohol and marijuana, I smoke a single cigarette, just to show that I can do it. This becomes a sort of parlor trick, one cigarette every few weeks. My wife marvels. I marvel. My will seems indestructible, except when I am high or asleep and it relaxes.

Yes, I still dream about smoking, but one night I dream that the cigarette doesn't taste good and I crush it out.

Perhaps that is a step forward. Here is a more recent dream:

I am running in some very long race, perhaps the Boston Marathon. There is no limit to my endurance. My wind is endless. While running I think: not smoking has made all the difference. The race ends. My position doesn't matter. What is important is that I have finished. There are many women at the finish line. None of them cares about my lungs, none looks at my heaving handsome hairy chest. Without exception they stare at my feet. I follow their eyes to the pools of blood in which I am standing. The women remove my shoes and socks. My feet are raw. The women bathe the bleeding sores with alcohol and then bandage the cleansed wounds. One whispers, "You should take better care of your feet."

That was a dream without cigarettes, but in most I smoke, and often when I awaken I wonder which is more real, the dream or the reality. Life without cigarettes is a fantasy. I never really wake up—not the way I did when I used to smoke that first cigarette of the day as if I were biting into an alarm clock.

It is time for my next appointment with the periodontist. He says my gums are looking still worse, bleeding too much, healing too slowly. He says the condition may come from too much alcohol but asks if cuts anyplace else on my body are healing slowly. I tell him I have just this morning picked a scab off my leg from a scrape received several weeks ago. He says that *is* slow and asks if I have had a thorough physical lately. "There's always the chance of diabetes," he adds.

Under nitrous oxide it is amusing to think that one could get diabetes from giving up smoking, via alcohol. But when the gas is turned off and I return to the office, I call my doctor, my real doctor, for an appointment. He tests my urine, my blood, the parts of my body. I don't have diabetes. I don't have anything. I am in good shape, except for being a little heavy—always this emphasis on shape, as if I am a piece of sculpture. He probes the shape of my mind, too, this phrenologist. Why am I drinking? What do I want? What do I *really* want?

What do I want? What does *he* want? What do *they*

want? What, per day, is the minimum requirement of love? Of hatred? Of self-hatred? I want cigarettes to love me, as I love them, even if I have rejected them. If the dentists I know all want to be medical doctors, the medical doctors want to be psychiatrists, and, I suppose, the psychiatrists want to be God. I skip out of his office knowing that, no matter how much excess weight I'm carrying, there's no excess sugar in my blood.

On the street a distinguished-looking man passes me, smoking a pipe. An expensive one, I'm sure. How smug he looks, with his moustache bristles standing at attention above the pipe. How contented. It occurs to me that smoking a pipe—all that fuss, all that bother, all that biting —may be his way of dealing with a lack of contentment. He may have diabetes. A lack of contentment. Is that dentist right? Am I an alcoholic? Do I perhaps use not smoking to legitimize drinking?

Another friend of ours gives up smoking. My wife says that now this friend is less agreeable, that she's always yawning into the phone and often drunk. As my wife speaks, I realize that these criticisms are intended to apply to me as well as our friend. At our age—the friend's and mine—it is as dangerous to stop smoking as to continue. But not at my son's age. I keep telling him to stop *now*.

One night he walks into the living room, what I have called the parlor, where I am doing my parlor trick, that one cigarette I occasionally—for no particular occasion— permit myself. He beams. He is so happy to see me smoking. Perhaps now I will stop bugging him.

A friend, yet another friend, is telling a story about the Depression. It concerns a man who lived for two years in the Camels sign above Times Square, the sign which blew smoke rings out into Broadway. Every evening he would dress up, Homburg and all, as if visiting his office, and go to the top floor, and then, after the elevator left, climb an iron ladder to the sign above the building, and sleep beneath the warm lights, basking there. My son loves this story, as I do, as everyone does. This is an un-smug, un-discontented man dealing with an un-smug, un-discontented sign. Neither man nor sign has ever thought about gums, diabetes, cancer

Though I tell my wife and son otherwise, not smoking is, at the moment, more expensive than smoking. There are the doctors' bills, the mounting cost of alcohol and food, and now I must go to the tailor again to have the new suits let out. He, too, studies my shape. He says that if he lets the suits out I will just go on eating too much, that I looked better when I was smoking.

I try a new parlor trick: two cigarettes. I can take them or leave them. Two is no harder than one. Soon I discover that three is no harder than two. But always they are someone else's, the American filters of my wife or a friend, never my beloved Gauloises. Finally, after almost two years of not smoking, except for these tiny lapses and after this recapitulation of other brands, I buy a pack of Gauloises—just to have them around.

How quickly that pack goes. At first I allow myself one cigarette after each meal. Within a week I am smoking one before breakfast. The experience is dizzying. It is like being on top of a mountain, a mountain which it took two years to climb and which will take perhaps two weeks to descend. I check the speed of my descent. I try to stay high on the mountain. Up there—smoking more, but still only occasionally, still measuring the cigarettes out by half-packs per day—smoking is a new experience. It is a high. Reality—the reality of smoking all the time—still seems far away, far below. I can still taste and smell. As never before, the Gauloises leave their taste in my mouth, their smell in the room.

One weekend I drive my son to college. After lunch I join him in having one cigarette. Suddenly the highway signs become significant, the way they might on marijuana. Each sign contains a message with many levels of meaning: TOURIST INFORMATION. DIVIDED HIGHWAY ENDS. REST AREA. Even the speed limits, changing up and down, are significant.

At some point, we are behind a car with a large barrel on its side in the baggage compartment, the cover of which is tied down as far as it can go. We try to guess what's in the barrel. My son thinks beer. I think nails. Whatever it is, we agree that it must be very heavy and wonder how it was lifted into position. When the car turns off the highway we can see the top of the barrel. It is open and empty. This, too, seems significant.

Though I would like to preserve the sense of elation I feel now when I smoke, as slowly as the movement of smoke itself I drift back to a pack a day, then two. My body is confused. It does not yet know if I have definitely returned to smoking. At times I still become dizzy. The dizziness echoes my indecision. The appeal of this dizziness is as much a return to childhood—merry-go-rounds, see-saws, etc.—as is having something in my mouth. For a day I don't smoke at all, telling myself that I want only to be dizzy the next day. I tell myself other things too on other days when I stop—for example, that I cannot be a little bit in prison, have, say, one foot in prison, but that I must choose between freedom and imprisonment.

An older man tells me that he, too, was addicted to smoking until he had to give it up for his health. For a while, without cigarettes, he says he couldn't read, write, make a phone call, make love. He talks about a surgeon who, after giving up smoking, forgets the procedure half-way through a complicated lung operation. The surgeon excuses himself from the operating room, smokes a dizzy-ing but exhilarating cigarette, remembers the procedure, and returns. It is a story I understand too well.

But all stories seem to be about smoking. I read Benjamin Constant's *Adolphe,* concerning his ambivalence in break-ing off affairs with Mme. de Charrière and later Mme. de Staël. For me now, these lovely ladies might as well be Gauloises. "Constant l'inconstant," my anti-hero.

Some days I put my cigarettes and matches and ashtrays away. On other days I bring them out. As I perform these rituals, I wonder if I must spend the rest of my life under tyrannical rule, either internal or external, a slave to my own will or to that of nicotine. Not to smoke at all and to be free are not the same thing. To be free is to be free to smoke or not and that, I know, is a freedom I no longer have. And yet I like to tell myself that to be free is to be able to make decisions, that each cigarette I smoke is as much a confirmation of my freedom as those I don't smoke.

When I try to stop, I can no longer tell myself that I have just finished a cigarette. I know that I didn't smoke for two years, that in smoking I express both a desire for pleasure and a fatalistic acceptance of death. Smoking is as much an ambivalent gesture of sensuality and unconcern as it is physically a mixture of stimulation and disgust. Smoking or not smoking is an inaccurate metaphor for dying or living, unless, as I do, one accepts death as part of life.

I TAKE MY WIFE on another trip to Paris. There she insists that a vacation is the time to stop smoking. One is less nervous, she says. I reply that my smoking has nothing to do with nervousness but with pleasure. I tell her how much I enjoy Gauloises at the source, how much I enjoy Cuban cigars here where they can be bought. The vacation goes up in smoke.

When we return we learn that a close friend has inoperable lung cancer. We visit him in the hospital. Forcing a smile, he asks his wife if he should put his sperm in a sperm bank. He presents various arguments. Pro: another baby for her, his posthumous child. Con: the possibility that cancer is genetic. He speaks of cancer as casually as if it were a headache or the "walking pneumonia" that the doctors at first thought he had; of cobalt treatments as casually as aspirin. The casualness is desperate, the humor black as tar, black as the disease consuming his lungs. His laughter is half coughing. When we leave, I say a silent prayer for him, for me, for all of us. And I begin to smoke more than ever.

For several days I smoke incessantly and then, at four packs a day, I stop. An agonizing day creeps by, two, three . . . a week . . . two weeks. It is much harder to give up smoking the second time. There is nothing to prove. One thinks he can do it, he has done it before. One clings to that fantasy of exact duplication and forgets that in nature there is only approximate cyclical repetition, that exact repetition is the ally of death. Even stopping smoking, restopping, which would seem to be an affirmation of life, must be a new living experience.

I am living it. Now many weeks have passed since my last cigarette. Again I am thinking about cigarettes all the time, every day, and I am dreaming about them at night. In one dream I study my teeth, the color of tobacco. And then suddenly I am tobacco, and I am packed into a cigarette, one among many insignificant particles. In a sweat I fight my way out of the paper cage. When I awaken I reach once again for a cigarette as if for an electric switch that isn't there, and after meals to wash down the food, and at cocktails to lighten the load of the alcohol.

Less incessantly now my body howls its pain and deprivation. It gets up in the morning, it absorbs its food and drink, it does what it has to do, it functions without cigarettes. I begin to think that I could no longer enjoy a cigarette; they smell bad. I wonder if cigarettes, like whiskey, are an acquired taste, a taste which one must learn not to taste. But I don't dare test this theory. I am in a position where I can neither enjoy smoking nor not smoking. I can enjoy only the illusion of absolute freedom.

An almost full carton of Gauloises remains in my desk at the office, and two cartons at home. After so many years I came to think of smoking as positively useful and productive. With the burning of each cigarette, the crushing of each empty pack, the discarding of each empty carton, there was a sense of real progress. But now I am not sure if smoking the remaining cigarettes or discarding them would be the greater waste.

I don't know whether I will ever smoke again. I can imagine being sentenced to death (by some external force rather than by life itself) and being offered a last cigarette. Perhaps my hands are tied. Perhaps I am blindfolded. I can imagine parting my lips, as I have so many times before, and accepting the cigarette. I can also imagine refusing it.

As for Poets

Gary Snyder

As for Poets,
The Earth Poets,
Who write small poems,
Need help from no man.

§

The Air Poets
Play on the swiftest gales
And sometimes loll in the eddies.
Poem after poem
Curling back on the same thrust.

§

At fifty below
Fuel oil won't flow
And propane stays in the tank.
Fire poets
Burn at absolute zero
Fossil love pumped back up.

§

The first
Water poet
Stayed down six years.
He was covered with seaweed.
The life in his poem
Left millions of tiny
Different tracks
Criss-crossing through the mud.

§

With the Sun and Moon
In his belly,

The Space Poet,
Sleeps.
No end to the sky—
But his poems,
Like wild geese,
Fly off the edge.

§

A Mind Poet
Stays in the house.
The house is empty
And it has no walls.
The poem
Is seen from all sides,
Everywhere,
At once.

A Project for Freight Trains

David Young

Sitting at crossings and waiting for freights to pass, we have all noticed words—COTTON BELT / ERIE / BE SPECIFIC—SAY UNION PACIFIC / SOUTHERN SERVES THE SOUTH—going by. I propose to capitalize on this fact in the following way:

All freight cars that have high, solid sides—boxcars, refrigerator cars, tank cars, hopper cars, cement cars—should be painted one of eight attractive colors, and have one large word printed on them:

1. Burnt orange freightcars with the word CLOUD in olive drab.

2. Peagreen freightcars with the word STAR in charcoal gray.

3. Rose-red freightcars with the word MEADOW in salmon pink.

4. Glossy black freightcars with the word STEAM in gold.

5. Peach-colored freightcars with the word AIR in royal blue.

6. Peach-colored freightcars with the word PORT in forest green.

7. Lavender freightcars with the word GRASS in vermilion or scarlet.

8. Swiss-blue freightcars with the word RISING in chocolate brown.

When this has been accomplished, freightcars should continue to be used in the usual ways, so that the word and color combinations will be entirely random, and unpredictable poems will roll across the landscape.

Freightcars without words (i.e., without high or solid sides, such as flatcars, cattlecars, gondolas, automobile transporters, etc.) should all be painted white, to emphasize their function as spaces in the poems. Cabooses can be this color too, with a large black dot, the only punctuation.

Approximations of these random train poems can be arrived at by using the numbers above, plus 9 and 0 for spaces, and combining serial numbers from dollar bills, social security numbers, birthdates, and telephone numbers.

This project would need to be carried out over the entire United States at once. Every five years a competition could be held among poets to see who can provide the best set of colors and words for the coming year.

Homemade

Ian McEwan

I CAN SEE NOW our cramped, overlit bathroom and Connie with a towel draped round her shoulders, sitting on the edge of the bath weeping, while I filled the sink with warm water and whistled—such was my elation—"Teddy Bear" by Elvis Presley, I can remember, I have always been able to remember, fluff from the candlewick bedspread swirling on the surface of the water, but only lately have I fully realized that if this was the *end* of a particular episode, insofar as real-life episodes may be said to have an end, it was Raymond who occupied, so to speak, the beginning and middle, and if in human affairs there are no such things as episodes, then I should really insist that this story is about Raymond and not about virginity, coitus, incest, and self-abuse. So let me begin by telling you that it was ironic, for reasons which will become apparent only very much later—and you must be patient—it was ironic that Raymond of all people should want to make me aware of my virginity. In Finsbury Park one day Raymond approached me, and steering me across to some laurel bushes, bent and unbent his finger mysteriously before my face and watched me intently as he did so. I looked on blankly. Then I bent and unbent my finger too and saw that it was the right thing to do because Raymond beamed.

"You get it?" he said. "You get it!" Driven by his exhilaration I said yes, hoping then that Raymond would leave me alone now to bend and unbend my finger, to come at some understanding of his bewildering digital allegory in solitude. Raymond grasped my lapels with unusual intensity.

"What about it then?" he gasped. Playing for time, I

crooked my forefinger again and slowly straightened it, cool and sure, in fact so cool and sure that Raymond held his breath and stiffened with its motion. I looked at my erect finger and said,

"That depends," wondering if I was to discover today what it was we were talking of.

Raymond was fifteen then, a year older than I was, and though I counted myself his intellectual superior—which was why I had to pretend to understand the significance of his finger—it was Raymond who *knew* things, it was Raymond who conducted my education. It was Raymond who initiated me into the secrets of adult life which he understood himself intuitively but never totally. The world he showed me, all its fascinating detail, lore and sin, the world for which he was a kind of standing master of ceremonies, never really suited Raymond. He knew that world well enough, but it—so to speak—did not want to know him. So when Raymond produced cigarettes, it was I who learned to inhale the smoke deeply, to blow smoke rings, and to cup my hand round the match like a film star while Raymond choked and fumbled; and later on when Raymond first got hold of some marijuana, of which I had never heard, it was I who finally got stoned into euphoria while Raymond admitted—something I would never have done myself—that he felt nothing at all. And again, while it was Raymond with his deep voice and wisp of beard who got us into horror films, he would sit through the show with his fingers in his ears and his eyes shut. And that was remarkable in view of the fact that in one month alone we saw twenty-two horror films. When Raymond stole a bottle of whiskey from a supermarket in order to introduce me to alcohol, I giggled drunkenly for two hours at Raymond's convulsive fits of vomiting. My first pair of long trousers were a pair belonging to Raymond which he had given to me as a present on my thirteenth birthday. On Raymond they had, like all his clothes, stopped four inches short of his ankles, bulged at the thigh, bagged at the groin, and now, as if a parable for our friendship, they fitted me like tailor-mades, in fact, so well did they fit me, so comfortable did they feel, that I wore no other trousers for a year.

And then there were the thrills of shoplifting. The idea, as explained to me by Raymond, was quite simple. You walked into Foyle's bookshop, crammed your pockets with books, and took them to a dealer on the Mile End Road who was pleased to give you half their cost price. For the very first occasion I borrowed my father's overcoat, which trailed the pavement magnificently as I swept along. I met Raymond outside the shop. He was in shirtsleeves because he had left his coat on the underground, but he was certain he could manage without one anyway, so we went into the shop. While I stuffed into my many pockets a selection of slim volumes of prestigious verse, Raymond was concealing on his person the seven volumes of the Variorum Edition of *The Works of Edmund Spenser*. For anyone else the boldness of the act might have offered some chance of success, but Raymond's boldness had a precarious quality, closer in fact to a complete detachment from the realities of the situation. The under-manager stood behind Raymond as he plucked the books from the shelf. The two of them were standing by the door as I brushed by with my own load, and I gave Raymond, who still clasped the tomes about him, a conspiratorial smile, and thanked the under-manager, who automatically held the door open for me. Fortunately, so hopeless was Raymond's attempt at shoplifting, so idiotic and transparent his excuses, that the manager finally let him go, liberally assuming him to be, I suppose, mentally deranged.

And finally, and perhaps most significantly, Raymond acquainted me with the dubious pleasures of masturbation. At the time I was twelve, the dawn of my sexual day. We were exploring a cellar on a bomb site, poking around to see what the dossers had left behind, when Raymond, having lowered his trousers as if to have a piss, began to rub his prick with a coruscating vigor, inviting me to do the same. I did, and soon became suffused with a warm, indistinct pleasure which intensified to a floating, melting sensation, as if my guts might at any time drift away to nothing. And all this time our hands pumped furiously. I was beginning to congratulate Raymond on his discovery of such a simple, inexpensive, yet pleasurable way of passing the time, and at the same time wondering if I could not dedicate my whole life to this glorious sensation—and I suppose looking back now, I suppose that in many respects I have—I was about to express all manner of things when I was lifted by the scruff of the neck, my arms, my legs, my insides, hailed, twisted, wracked, and producing for all this two dollops of sperm which flipped over Raymond's Sunday jacket—it was Sunday—and dribbled into his breast pocket.

"Hey," he said, breaking with his action. "What did you do that for?" Still recovering from this devastating experience, I said nothing, I could not say anything.

"I show you how to do this," harangued Raymond, dabbing delicately at the glistening gisum on his dark jacket, "and all you can do is spit."

And so by the age of fourteen I had acquired, with Raymond's guidance, a variety of pleasures which I rightly associated with the adult world. I smoked about ten cigarettes a day, I drank whiskey when it was available, I had a connoisseur's taste for violence and obscenity, I had smoked the heady resin of *cannabis sativa,* and I was aware of my own sexual precocity, though oddly it never occurred to me to find any use for it, my imagination as yet unnourished by longings or private fantasies. And all these pastimes were financed by the dealer in the Mile End Road. For these acquired tastes Raymond was my Mephistopheles, he was a clumsy Vergil to my Dante, showing me the way to a Paradiso where he himself could not tread. He could not smoke because it made him cough, the whiskey made him ill, the films frightened or bored him, the cannabis did not affect him, and while I made stalactites on the ceiling of the bomb site cellar, he made nothing at all.

"Perhaps," he said mournfully, as we were leaving the site one afternoon, "perhaps I'm a little too old for that sort of thing."

So WHEN RAYMOND stood before me now, intently crooking and straightening his finger, I sensed that here was yet another fur-lined chamber of that vast, gloomy, and delectable mansion, adulthood, and that if I only held back a little, concealing, for pride's sake, my ignorance, then shortly Raymond would reveal and then shortly I would excel.

"Well, that depends . . ." We walked across Finsbury Park, where once Raymond, in his earlier, delinquent days, had fed glass splinters to the pigeons, where together, in innocent bliss worthy of *The Prelude*, we had roasted alive Sheila Harcourt's budgerigar while she swooned on the grass nearby, where as young boys we had crept behind bushes to hurl rocks at the couples fucking in the arbor; across Finsbury Park then, and Raymond saying, "Who do you know?"

Who did I know? I was still blundering, and this could be a change of subject, for Raymond had an imprecise mind. So I said, "Who do *you* know?" to which Raymond replied "Lulu Smith" and made everything clear—or at least the subject matter, for my innocence was remarkable. Lulu Smith! Dinky Lulu! The very name curls a chilly hand round my balls. Lulu Lamour, of whom it was said she would do anything, and that she had done everything. There were Jewish jokes, Elephant jokes, and there were Lulu jokes, and these were mainly responsible for the extravagant legend. Lulu Slim—but how my mind reels—whose physical enormity was matched only by the enormity of her reputed sexual appetite and prowess, her grossness only by the grossness she inspired, the legend only by the reality. Zulu Lulu! who—so fame had it—had lain a trail across North London of frothing idiots, a desolation row of broken minds and pricks spanning Shepherd's Bush to Holloway, Ongar to Islington. Lulu! her wobbling girth and laughing piggies' eyes, blooming thighs, and dimpled finger joints, this heaving, steaming leg-load of schoolgirl flesh who had, so reputation insisted, had it with a giraffe, a hummingbird, a man in an iron lung (who had subsequently died), a yak, Cassius Clay, a marmoset, a Mars bar, and the gearstick of her grandfather's Morris Minor (and subsequently a traffic warden).

Finsbury Park was filled with the spirit of Lulu Smith, and I felt for the first time ill-defined longings as well as mere curiosity. I knew approximately what was to be done, for had I not seen heaped couples in all corners of the park during the long summer evenings, and had I

not thrown stones and water bombs?—something I now
superstitiously regretted. And suddenly there in Finsbury
Park, as we threaded our way through the pert piles of
dog shit, I was made aware of and resented my virginity;
I knew it to be the last room in the mansion, I knew it to
be for certain the most luxurious, its furnishings more
elaborate than any other room, its attractions more deadly,
and the fact that I had never had it, made it, done it,
was a total anathema, my malodorous albatross, and I
looked to Raymond, who still held his forefinger stiff
before him, to reveal what I must do. Raymond was bound
to know.

After school Raymond and I went to a cafe near Finsbury Park Odeon. While others of our age picked their
noses over their stamp collections or homework, Raymond
and I spent many hours here, discussing mostly easy ways
of making money, and drinking large mugs of tea. Sometimes we got talking to the workmen who came there.
Millais should have been there to paint us as we listened
transfixed to their unintelligible fantasies and exploits, of
deals with lorry drivers, lead from church roofs, fuel
missing from the City Engineer's department, and then
of cunts, bits, skirt, of strokings, beatings, fuckings, suck-
ings, of arses and tits, behind, above, below, in front, with,
without, of scratching and tearing, licking and shitting,
of juiced cunts streaming, warm and infinite, of others
cold and arid but worth a try, of pricks old and limp, or
young and ebullient, of coming, too soon, too late, or not
at all, of how many times a day, of attendant diseases, of
pus and swellings, cankers and regrets, of poisoned ovaries
and destitute testicles; we listened to who and how the
dustmen fucked, how the Co-op milkmen fitted it in, what
the coalmen could hump, what the carpet fitter could lay,
what the builders could erect, what the meter man could
inspect, what the bread man could deliver, the gas man sniff
out, the plumber plumb, the electrician connect, the doctor
inject, the lawyer solicit, the furniture man install—and so
on, in an unreal complex of timeworn puns and innuendo,
formulas, slogans, folklore, and bravado. I listened without
understanding, remembering and filing away anecdotes
which I would one day use myself, putting by histories

of perversions and sexual manners—in fact, a whole sexual morality, so that when finally I began to understand, from my own experience, what it was all about, I had on tap a complete education which, augmented by a quick reading of the more interesting parts of Havelock Ellis and Henry Miller, earned me the reputation of being the juvenile connoisseur of coitus to whom dozens of males—and fortunately females, too—came to seek advice. And all this, a reputation which followed me into art college and enlivened my career there, all this after only one fuck—the subject of this story.

So it was there in the cafe where I had listened, remembered, and understood nothing that Raymond now relaxed his forefinger at last to curl it round the handle of his cup and said,

"Lulu Smith will let you see it for a shilling."

I was glad of that. I was glad we were not rushing into things, glad that I would not be left alone with Zulu Lulu and be expected to perform the terrifyingly obscure, glad that the first encounter of this necessary adventure would be reconnaissance. And besides, I had only ever seen two naked females in my life. The obscene films we patronized in those days were nowhere near obscene enough, showing only the legs, backs, and ecstatic faces of happy couples, leaving the rest to our tumescent imaginations and clarifying nothing. As for the two naked women, my mother was vast and grotesque, the skin hanging from her like flayed toad hides, and my ten-year-old sister was an ugly bat whom as a child I could hardly bring myself to look at, let alone share the bathtub with. And after all, a shilling was no expense at all, considering that Raymond and I were richer than most of the workmen in the cafe. In fact I was richer than any of my many uncles or my poor overworked father or anyone else I knew in my family. I used to laugh when I thought of the twelve-hour shift my father worked in the flour mill, of his exhausted, blanched, ill-tempered face when he got home in the evening, and I laughed a little louder when I thought of the thousands who each morning poured out of the terraced houses like our own to labor through the week, rest up on Sunday, and then back again on Monday

to toil in the mills, factories, timber yards, and quaysides
of London, returning each night older, more tired, and no
richer; over our cups of tea I laughed with Raymond at
this quiescent betrayal of a lifetime, heaving, digging,
shoving, packing, checking, sweating, and groaning for the
profits of others, at how, to reassure themselves, they made
a virtue of this lifetime's grovel, at how they prized themselves for never missing a day in the inferno; and most
of all I laughed when uncles Bob or Ted or my father
made me a present of one of their hard-earned shillings—
and on special occasions a half-pound note—I laughed
because I knew that a good afternoon's work in the bookshop earned more than they scraped together in a week.
I had to laugh discreetly, of course, for it would not do
to mess up a gift like that, especially when it was quite
obvious that they derived a great deal of pleasure from
giving it to me. I can see them now, one of my uncles or
my father striding the tiny length of the front parlor, the
coin or bank note in his hand, reminiscing, anecdoting,
and advising me on life, poised before the luxury of giving,
and feeling good, feeling so good that it was a joy to
watch. They felt, and for that short period they were,
grand, wise, reflective, kindhearted, and expansive, and
perhaps, who knows, a little divine; patricians dispensing
to their son or nephew in the wisest, most generous way,
the fruits of their sagacity and wealth—they were gods in
their own temple and who was I to refuse their gift?
Kicked in the arse round the factory fifty hours a week,
they needed these parlor miracle plays, these mythic con-
frontations between Father and Son, so I, being appreciative and sensible of all the nuances of the situation,
accepted their money, at the risk of boredom played along
a little, and suppressed my amusement till afterwards,
when I was made weak with tearful, hooting laughter.
Long before I knew it I was a student, a promising student,
of irony.

A SHILLING THEN was not too much to pay for a glimpse at
the incommunicable, the heart of mystery's mystery, the
Fleshly Grail, Dinky Lulu's pussy, and I urged Raymond
to arrange a viewing as soon as possible. Raymond was

already sliding into his role of stage manager, furrowing his brow in an important way, humming about dates, times, places, payments, and drawing ciphers on the back of an en-envelope. Raymond was one of those rare people who not only derive great pleasure from organizing events, but also are forlornly bad at doing it. It was quite possible that we would arrive on the wrong day at the wrong time, that there would be confusion about payment or the length of viewing time, but there was one thing which was ulti-mately more certain than anything else, more certain than the sun rising tomorrow, and that was that we would finally be shown the exquisite quim. For life was un-deniably on Raymond's side; while in those days I could not have put my feelings into so many words, I sensed that in the cosmic array of individual fates, Raymond's was cast diametrically opposite mine. Fortune played practical jokes on Raymond, perhaps she even kicked sand in his eyes, but she never spat in his face or trod deliberately on his existential corns—Raymond's mistakings, losses, be-trayals, and injuries were all, in the final estimate, comic rather than tragic. I remember one occasion when Ray-mond paid seventeen pounds for a two-ounce cake of hashish, which turned out not to be hashish at all. To cover his losses, Raymond took the lump to a well-known spot in Soho and tried to sell it to a plainclothesman, who fortunately did not press a charge. After all there was, at that time at least, no law against dealing in powdered horse dung, even if it was wrapped in tinfoil.

Then there was the cross-country. Raymond was a medi-ocre runner and was among ten others chosen to represent the school in the sub-Counties meeting. I always went along to the meetings. In fact there was no other sport I watched with such good heart, such entertainment and elation, as a good cross-country. I loved the wracked, contorted faces of the runners as they came up the tunnel of flags and crossed the finish line; I found especially inter-esting those who came after the first fifty or so, running harder than any of the other contestants and competing demonically among themselves for the hundred and thir-teenth place in the field. I watched them stumble up the tunnel of flags, clawing at their throats, retching, flailing their arms, and falling to the grass, convinced that I had before me here a vision of human futility. Only the first thirty runners counted for anything in the contest, and once the last of these had arrived the group of spectators began to disperse, leaving the rest to fight their private battles—and it was at this point that my interest pricked up. Long after the judges, marshals, and timekeepers had gone home, I remained at the finish line in the descending gloom of a late winter's afternoon to watch the last of the runners crawl across the end marker. Those who fell I helped to their feet, I gave handkerchiefs to bloody noses, I thumped vomiters on the back, I massaged cramped calves and toes—a real Florence Nightingale, in fact, with the difference that I felt an elation, a gay fascination with the triumphant spirit of human losers who had run them-selves into the ground for nothing at all. How my mind soared, how my eyes swam when, after having waited ten, fifteen, even twenty minutes in that vast, dismal field, surrounded on all sides by factories, pylons, dull houses, and garages, a cold wind rising, bringing the beginnings of a bitter drizzle, waiting there in that heavy gloom—and then suddenly to discern on the far side of the field a limp white blob slowly making its way to the tunnel, slowly measuring out with numb feet on the wet grass its micro-destiny of utter futility. And there beneath the brooding metropolitan sky, as if to unify the complex totality of organic evolution and human purpose and place it within my grasp, the tiny amoebic blob across the field took on human shape, and yet still it held to the same purpose, staggering determinedly in its pointless effort to reach the flags—just life, just faceless, self-renewing life to which, as the figure jackknifed to the ground by the finishing line, my heart warmed, my spirit rose in the abandonment of morbid and fatal identification with the cosmic life process—the Logos.

"Bad luck, Raymond," I would say cheerily as I handed him his sweater, "better luck next time." And smiling wanly with the sure, sad knowledge of Arlecchino, of Feste, the knowledge that of the two it is the Comedian not the Tragedian who holds the Trump, the twenty-second Arcanum, whose letter is Than, whose symbol is Sol, smiling as we left the now almost dark field Raymond would say,

"Well it was only a cross-country, only a game you know."

RAYMOND PROMISED to confront the divine Lulu Smith with our proposition the following day after school, and since I was pledged to look after my sister that evening while my parents were at the Walthamstow dog track, I said good-bye to Raymond there at the cafe. All the way home I thought about cunt. I saw it in the smile of the conductress, I heard it in the roar of the traffic, I smelled it in the fumes from the shoe polish factory, conjectured it beneath the skirts of passing housewives, felt it at my fingertips, sensed it in the air, drew it in my mind, and at supper, which was toad-in-the-hole, I devoured, as in an unspeakable rite, genitalia of batter and sausage. And for all this I still did not know just exactly what a cunt was. I eyed my sister across the table. I exaggerated a little just now when I said she was an ugly bat—I was beginning to think that perhaps she was not so bad-looking after all. Her teeth protruded, that could not be denied, and if her cheeks were a little too sunken, it was not so you would notice in the dark, and when her hair had been washed, as it was now, you could almost pass her off as plain. So it was not surprising that I came to be thinking over my toad-in-the-hole that with some cajoling and perhaps a little honest deceit, Connie could be persuaded to think of herself, if only for a few minutes, as something more than a sister, as, let us say, a beautiful young lady, a film star, and maybe, Connie, we could slip into bed here and try out this rather moving scene, now you get out of these clumsy pajamas while I see to the light . . . And armed with this comfortably gained knowledge, I could face the awesome Lulu with zeal and abandon, the whole terrifying ordeal would pale into insignificance, and who knows, perhaps I could lay her out there and then, halfway through the peepshow.

I never enjoyed looking after Connie. She was petulant, demanding, spoiled, and wanted to play games all the while instead of watching the television. I usually managed to get to bed an hour early by winding the clock forward. Tonight I wound it back. As soon as my mother and father had left for the dog track, I asked Connie which games she would like to play, she could choose anything she liked.

"I don't want to play games with you."

"Why not?"

"Because you were staring at me all the time through supper."

"Well of course I was, Connie. I was trying to think of the games you liked to play best, and I was just looking at you, that was all." Finally she agreed to play hide-and-seek, which I had suggested with special insistence because our house was of such a size that there were only two rooms you could hide in, and they were both bedrooms. Connie was to hide first. I covered my eyes and counted to thirty, listening all the while to her footsteps in my parents' bedroom directly above, hearing with satisfaction the creak of the bed—she was hiding under the eiderdown, her second favorite place. I shouted "coming" and began to mount the stairs. At the bottom of the stairs I do not think I had decided clearly what I was about to do; perhaps just look around, see where things were, draw a mental plan for future reference—after all, it would not do to go scaring my little sister, who would not think twice about telling my father everything, and that would mean a scene of some sort, laborious lies to invent, shouting and crying and that sort of thing, just at a time when I needed all my energy for the obsession in hand. By the time I reached the top of the stairs, however, the blood having drained from brain to groin, literally, one might say, from sense to sensibility, by the time I was catching my breath on the top stair and closing my moist hand round the bedroom door handle, I had decided to rape my sister. Gently I pushed the door open and called in a singsong voice,

"Connieeeeeeee, where aaare you?" That usually made her giggle, but this time there was no sound. Holding my breath, I tiptoed over to the bedside and sang,

"I knoooooow where youuuu are," and bending down

by the telltale lump under the eiderdown I whispered, "I'm coming to get you," and began to peel the bulky cover away, softly, almost tenderly, peeking into the dark warmth underneath. Dizzy with expectation I drew it right back, and there, helplessly and innocently stretched out before me, were my parents' pajamas, and even as I was leaping back in surprise I received a blow in the small of my back of such unthinking vigor as can only be inflicted by a sister on her brother. And there was Connie with mirth, the wardrobe door swinging open behind her.

"I saw you, I saw you, and you didn't see me!" To relieve my feelings I kicked her shins and sat on the bed to consider what next, while Connie, predictably histrionic, sat on the floor and boo-hooed. I found the noise depressing after a while, so I went downstairs and read the paper, certain that soon Connie would follow me down. She did and she was sulking.

"What game do you want to play now?" I asked her. She sat on the edge of the sofa, pouting and sniffing and hating me. I was even considering forgetting the whole plan and giving myself up to an evening's television when I had an idea, an idea of such simplicity, elegance, clarity, and formal beauty, an idea which wore the assurance of its own success like a tailor-made suit. There is a game which all home-loving, unimaginative little girls like Connie find irresistible, a game which, ever since she had learned to speak the necessary words, Connie had plagued me to play with her, so that my boyhood years were haunted by her pleadings and exorcised by my inevitable refusals, it was a game, in short, which I would rather be burned at the stake for than have my friends see me play it. And now at last we were going to play Mummies and Daddies.

"*I* know a game you'd like to play, Connie," I said. Of course she would not reply, but I let my words hang there in the air like bait.

"I know a game *you'd* like to play." She lifted her head. "What is it?"

"It's a game you're always wanting to play."

She brightened. "Mummies and Daddies?" She was transformed, she was ecstatic. She fetched prams, dolls, stoves, fridges, cots, teacups, a washing machine, and a kennel from her room and set them up around me in a flutter of organizational zeal.

"Now you go here, no there, and this can be the kitchen and this is the door where you come in and don't tread on there because there's a wall and I come in and see you and I say to you and then you say to me and you go out and I make lunch." I was plunged into the microcosm of the dreary, everyday, ponderous banalities, the horrifying, niggling details of the life of our parents and their friends, the life that Connie so dearly wanted to ape. I went to work and came back, I went to the pub and came back, I posted a letter and came back, I went to the shops and came back, I read a paper, I pinched the Bakelite cheeks of my progeny, I read another paper, pinched some more cheeks, went to work and came back. And Connie? She just cooked on the stove, washed up in the sink unit, washed, fed, put to sleep, and roused her sixteen dolls, and then poured some more tea—and she was happy. She was the intergalactic-earth-goddess-housewife, she owned and controlled all around her, she saw all, she knew all, she told me when to go out, when to come in, which room I was in, what to say, how and when to say it. She was happy. She was complete, I have never seen another human so complete, she smiled, wide-open, joyous, and innocent smiles which I have never seen since—she tasted paradise on earth. And one point she was so blocked with the wonder, the ecstasy of it all, that mid-sentence her words choked up and she sat back on her heels, her eyes glistening, and breathed one long musical sigh of rare and wonderful happiness. It was almost a shame I had it in mind to rape her. Returning from work the twentieth time that half hour I said,

"Connie, we're leaving out one of the most important things that Mummies and Daddies do together." She could hardly believe we had left anything out and she was curious to know.

"They fuck together, Connie, surely you know about that."

"Fuck?" On her lips the word sounded strangely meaningless, which in a way I suppose it was, as far as I was concerned. The whole idea was to give it some meaning.

"Fuck? What does that mean?"

"Well, it's what they do at night when they go to bed at night, just before they go to sleep."

"Show me."

I explained that we would have to go upstairs and get into bed.

"No we don't. We can pretend and this can be the bed," she said, pointing at a square made by the design of the carpet.

"I cannot pretend and show it to you at the same time." So once again I was climbing the stairs, once again my blood was pounding and my manhood proudly stirring. Connie was quite excited too, still delirious with the happiness of the game and pleased at the novel turn it was taking.

"The first thing they do," I said, as I led her to the bed, "is to take off all their clothes." I pushed her onto the bed and, with fingers almost useless with agitation, unbuttoned her pajamas till she sat naked before me, still sweet-smelling from her bath and giggling with the fun of it all. Then I got undressed too, leaving my pants on so as not to alarm her, and sat by her side. As children we had seen enough of each other's body to take our nakedness for granted, though that was some time ago now and I sensed her unease.

"Are you sure this is what they do?"

My own uncertainty was obscured now by lust. "Yes," I said, "it's quite simple. You have a hole there and I put my weenie in it."

She clasped her hand over her mouth giggling incredulously. "That's silly. Why do they want to do that?" I had to admit it to myself, there was something unreal about it.

"They do it because it's their way of saying they like each other." Connie was beginning to think that I was making the whole thing up, which, again, in a way I suppose I was. She stared at me wide-eyed.

"But that's daft, why don't they just tell each other?" I was on the defensive, a mad scientist explaining his new crackpot invention—coitus—before an audience of skeptical rationalists.

"Look," I said to my sister, "it's not only that. It's also a very nice feeling. They do it to get that feeling."

"To get the feeling?" She still did not quite believe me. "Get the feeling? What do you mean, get the feeling?"

I said, "I'll show you." And at the same time I pushed Connie onto the bed and lay on top of her in the manner I had inferred from the films Raymond and I had seen together. I was still wearing my underpants. Connie stared blankly up at me, not even afraid—in fact, she might have been closer to boredom. I writhed from side to side, trying to push my pants off without getting up.

"I still don't get it," she complained from underneath me. "I'm not getting any feeling. Are you getting any feeling?"

"Wait," I grunted, as I hooked the underpants round the end of my toes with the very tips of my fingers, "if you just wait a minute I'll show you." I was beginning to lose my temper with Connie, with myself, with the universe, but mostly with my underpants, which snaked determinedly round my ankles. At last I was free. My prick was hard and sticky on Connie's belly, and now I began to maneuver it between her legs with one hand while I supported the weight of my body with the other. I searched her tiny crevice without the least notion of what I was looking for, but half-expecting all the same to be transformed at any moment into a human whirlwind of sensation. I think perhaps I had in mind a warm fleshly chamber, but as I prodded and foraged, jabbed and wheedled, I found nothing other than tight, resisting skin. Meanwhile Connie just lay on her back, occasionally making little comments.

"Oh, that's where I go wee-wee. I'm sure *our* Mummy and Daddy don't do this." My supporting arm was being seared by pins and needles, I was feeling raw, and yet still I poked and pushed, in a mood of growing despair. Each time Connie said, "I still don't get any feeling," I felt another ounce of my manhood slip away. Finally I had to rest. I sat on the edge of the bed to consider my hopeless failure while behind me Connie propped herself up on her elbows. After a moment or two I felt the bed begin to shake with silent spasms and, turning, I saw

Connie with tears spilling down her screwed-up face, inarticulate and writhing with choked laughter.

"What is it?" I asked, but she could only point vaguely in my direction and groan, and then she lay back on the bed, heaving and helpless with mirth. I sat by her side, not knowing what to think but deciding, as Connie quaked behind me, that another attempt was now out of the question. At last she was able to get out some words. She sat up and pointed at my still erect prick and gasped,

"It looks so . . . it looks so . . ." She sank back in another fit, and then managed in one squeal,

"So silly it looks so silly," after which she collapsed again into a high-pitched, squeezed-out titter. I sat there in lonely detumescent blankness, numbed by this final humiliation into the realization that this was no real girl beside me, this was no true representative of that sex, this was no boy, certainly, nor was it finally a girl—it was my sister, after all. I stared down at my limp prick, wondering at its hangdog look, and just as I was thinking of getting my clothes together, Connie, silent now, touched me on the elbow.

"I know where it goes," she said, and lay back on the bed, her legs wide apart, something it had not occurred to me to ask her to do. She settled herself among the pillows.

"I know where the hole is." I forgot my sister and my prick rose inquisitively, hopefully, to the invitation that Connie was whispering. It was all right with her now, she was at Mummies and Daddies and controlling the game again. With her hand she guided me into her tight, dry little-girl's cunt and we lay perfectly still for a while. I wished Raymond could have seen me, and I was glad he had brought my virginity to my notice, I wished Dinky Lulu could have seen me, in fact if my wishes had been granted I would have had all my friends, all the people I knew, file through the bedroom to catch me in my splendorous pose. For more than sensation, more than any explosion behind my eyes, spears through my stomach, searings in my groin, or wrackings of my soul—more than any of these things, none of which I felt anyway, more than even the thought of these things, I felt proud, proud to be fucking, even if it were only Connie, my ten-year-old sister, even if it had been a crippled mountain goat, I would have been proud to be lying there in that manly position, proud in advance of being able to say "I have fucked," of belonging intimately and irrevocably to that superior half of humanity who had known coitus, and fertilized the world with it. Connie lay quite still, too, her eyes half closed, breathing deeply—she was asleep. It was way past her bedtime and our strange game had exhausted her. For the first time I moved gently backwards and forwards, just a few times, and came in a miserable, played-out, barely pleasurable way. It woke Connie into indignation.

"You've wet inside me," and she began to cry. Hardly noticing, I got up and started to get dressed. This may have been one of the most desolate couplings known to copulating mankind, involving lies, deceit, humiliation, incest, my partner falling asleep, my gnat's orgasm and the sobbing which now filled the bedroom, but I was pleased with it, myself, Connie, pleased to let things rest a while, to let the matter drop. I led Connie to the bathroom and began to fill the sink—my parents would be back soon and Connie should be asleep in her bed. I had made it into the adult world finally, I was pleased about that, but right then I did not want to see a naked girl, or a naked anything for a while. Tomorrow I would tell Raymond to forget the appointment with Lulu, unless he wanted to go it alone. And I knew for a fact that he would not want that at all.

FOUR POEMS
BY MARILYN HACKER

To the Reader

PACING from room to room trimming the plants
I walk heavily on my heels. I smoke
foul-smelling French cigarettes. Invoke
that portly bluestocking in gardening pants.
Won't do. And if Catullus learns to cook
while Lesbia goes to the bars to cruise
you haven't put up anything to lose
except two hours to read a different book.
Boys will be boys and wonder in their rooms
if fame could be a sociable disease.
"I'll sleep alone and murder whom I please
and find another lover when the moon's
in Scorpio." Be grateful to our Mom.
She let you off with cancer and the Bomb.

Nimue to Merlin

WHO are you anyway? Did it take long
to get here? I don't live in a tower,
but I don't have Thursday salons either.
I take care of my plants. I'm not as young
as I look, and I like to be alone
most of the time. May I fix you a drink?

Shoo off the cat. I usually don't drink
before dinner, but I've had a long

day, working. Are you traveling alone?
I've heard about you. Once, I saw your tower
from the high road, when I was very young
and curious. I'm glad that I'm not either

now. And here you are, which means, you've either
changed, or you want something. I wouldn't drink
so fast if I were you. How young
you look. Your skin is like a boy's, and long
hair becomes you. If you stood up, you would tower
over me. Don't you find, when you're alone

long, you lose eyes and voices, let alone
people's tastes and smells. Excuse me, I'll either
embarrass myself or you. In your tower
when it's almost dawn, and you can't drink
or sleep more (I'm presuming) and it's a long
way down, and some idiotic young

bird shrills up, do you think, when you were young.
if you'd let it hurt, let well enough alone,
things would have gotten better before long?
You wouldn't be here now. I don't think so either.
Here's pears and cheese. I'll make another drink.
Your hands are cold. Your neck is stiff as a tower.

It's already late. The road back to the tower
is crowded with political loud young
men with no wives who've had too much to drink,
Do you want to go back there tonight alone?
I won't keep you. I won't chase you either.
Sometimes the nights here are extremely long.

Lie alongside me. I'll build you a tower
in my hand. You're either too old or too young
to be alone here. Open your mouth. Let me drink.

Aube Provençale

ABSENT, this morning
the cock crowed later than the nine o'clock
church bells. Cherry boughs

bronzed outside the casement,
and I woke

sweating, with my hands
between my thighs, from a dream
of archives, wanting you
under me, my breasts hollowed in the arc
below your ribs,

my knees between your knees,
my hands behind your ears, my cheek
furrowed in your chest, tasting
our mingled night-sweat, tasting
your sleep.

I'll make a song
on your neck-cords. Wake up,
bird asleep against my hip-bone,
and crow, it's already
morning.

Crépuscule Provençale

CURSING the Mistral
the neighbor elbows doorward.
It batters on tiled roofs, whips cascades
across the hill-face. Meet me
near the sea

I wrote, come to me
through polyglot gossip
and we'll share mountains, oceans, islands.
November is wind and rain
here. Heavy

persimmons, bloody
on black branches, gleamed in blue
afternoon, clear as a hidden valley.
Lapis beyond the green gorge, the sea spilled
its chalice

of hills. It's a month
since I left you, near water, wet
pebbles in our pockets, I'll write, our cheeks
brushed, salt gusts already
between us.

Dark now, shutters bang
stucco. Later I'll drink
by the fire, and let three tongues of
chatter silence an absence sung
in the wind.

The Inheritance

W. S. Merwin

On a mountain whose name had been forgotten, a shepherd found a book in a cave.

He had been gathering stones to make a wall across the cave mouth, when he found it. It was under the last stone of a pile in a corner of the cave. He had never seen a book before. He had never heard of such a thing. He was frightened and crept back a few steps toward the cave mouth, watching it.

He wanted to see whether it breathed. Whether it was a thing that breathed, and if it was, he wanted to see how long it could go without breathing. The first and second things he wanted to know.

He wanted to see whether it was really dead, or only pretending to be dead. He had seen animals pretending to be dead, looking like that but shaped differently, crouched together or coiled up underneath. He had seen men pretending to be dead, looking like that but shaped differently, lying there with weapons hidden under them. He had seen, worst of all, beings that looked like men, and even looked as though they were breathing, suddenly turn into stones or logs or shadows, and pretend to be dead, only to follow him later until he was unable to tell whether he was asleep or awake. But they too were shaped differently, like logs, or stones, or shadows. Even if it was alive, this was none of those things. It must be something else. So he wanted to see what it was.

Then he wanted to see whether it was a door. He had heard of doors, like doors into real houses, but doors into the floors of caves. This, if it was a door, was a door like an old lost garment of something, gone stiff now, and strange to everyone, smelling of unending darkness, and hostile to the infant present. It had been lying alone in the darkness too long, the only book.

If it was a door it was a door like food, lying in front of him, submissive but alien. It had a few rows of patterns pressed into it. Tracks.

He bent forward and put his ear to it and listened.

Things might sleep in those tracks now. Those might be their beds. The things might be out now, hunting, and come back to their beds, and he would be there. There would be many of them. He had heard of them, small people.

Maybe not, though.

He had heard of boxes. He began to want to know whether the thing was a box. He had even seen boxes. He had heard that some of the boxes still in the world had been found in dark hiding places, in caves. Some of them had had valuable things in them, and some had had terrible things in them, and death itself hiding under the lids. Against these last, he knew, no human weapons gave protection. But he pulled his staff closer. The sun was going down. There was no fire.

It was almost dark. He was afraid to touch the thing now with his hand. He was afraid to touch it just before night. But he was afraid to leave it. But he wanted to send the dog to bring the sheep up to the cave. But he couldn't bring the sheep into the cave now, with the book there. But already he could hardly see it. But when he moved forward, his own shadow, which for some time had been nothing but a shapeless cloud of darkness, moved forward also and covered the book. But he heard the sheep rustling and coughing outside the cave, lambs crying, not near enough. But he listened for the dog. But he could not hear it. But he thought of the night coming. Outside, in that part of his mind, stars were walking forward toward night until their lights were visible, and they came on walking, and stopped in their places, and then night carried them toward the mountains.

He listened for the fox.

He listened for the wolf.

He heard the wind that came after sundown and then went away by itself.

Then he wanted to hear whether he heard breathing in the cave that wasn't his own breathing.

But then it seemed to have stopped.

He was listening. He was watching the place where he had last seen the thing, trying to remember exactly what it looked like.

But he kept thinking of wolves. There was one wolf he had seen many times, and he wanted to know whether it was the same wolf every time. Wherever he was, it always came alone, just at evening. He had never seen it come. Each time he had looked up and it was there, watching somewhere to one side of him. Each time he had fixed his eyes on the wolf, kept them there, almost stopped breathing, only to see, some time later, that he was watching a wolf-shaped patch of darkness, from which the animal had gone. He thought now that he must still be watching the wolf.

When the first light came into the cave he could see nothing at all in front of him. Then he felt his cheeks. They were wet with tears. Then he saw the book, and without waiting he crossed the cave, and bent down, and touched the book, and made his hand stay there. He felt a small animal, a small lightning, run up his arm, but it was not painful. He moved his fingers over the tracks. Then he straightened and put the fingers of his left hand into the palm of his right hand, and folded the fingers of his right hand over them, to comfort them, to talk with them and ask them. With one hand in the other, that way, he went out of the cave and down the slope.

The sheep were scattered. When he called the dog, he felt the tracks stir in the fingertips of his left hand. They stirred every time he called the dog. When the dog came it seemed to be afraid of him.

When he had the sheep together again, and the dog watching them, up by the cave, he went in to the book, and with both hands lifted an edge. When the book fell open, he knelt to look at the tracks. Many animals seemed to have passed there and he did not know any of them. When he tried to lift again, pages turned and the tracks went on. He came to the empty pages at the end. He knocked to see whether the bottom page was hollow. He lifted it and the whole book came up and he carried it out into the sunlight.

After that his life changed.

He stared at the book for hours every day. He wrapped it carefully in his sack when he changed pastures. He began to be able to remember some of the tracks. He thought there was a secret in them that he would discover. He looked for them in the world and sometimes he saw them, but alone, or in a different order, so that he thought the others must have disappeared. He began to remember the order in which the tracks came on the pages, and some of their repetitions, some of the groups in which they traveled together, some of the companies in which some of the groups traveled.

He thought he was coming closer all the time to learning the secret in the book which was making the book change his life.

But the book had infected him with a new fear—of losing it. He guarded it carefully. He avoided other shepherds. They became suspicious of him. They spied on him. They followed him. They saw the book. They saw him open it, stare at it, kneel, staring at it. They stole it from him. They killed his dog so that he would not be able to follow them. They tried to kill him. He got away at night. He went on until nobody knew his language. He was beaten. Everything else was taken away from him. He was found in a marketplace, begging. As he sat there he tried to trace some of the lost tracks in the dust, to remember them. He was seized. He was taken away and tortured, while they kept asking him questions he did not understand. The tortures were stopped and an old man led him away to a tent and gave him food and had him washed and dressed in clean clothes. The next morning they set out, and he with them. They traveled for days, into the mountains. Everything got older. They came to ancient rocks, ancient trees, a huge ruin. A man even older than the first one seemed to be the king there.

They led him to understand, with gestures, that they wanted him to trace the tracks, in the dust. The old king came to watch him make the marks, and stared at them, and asked the shepherd questions he did not understand.

They tried to teach him their language so that he could explain what the tracks meant, because the old king had heard of writing. They tried to learn his language, in case the meaning of the tracks could be spoken only in his language. They learned to trace the tracks themselves, to be ready for the day when he would be able to tell their meaning.

He showed them the tracks again, here and there in the world, and he saw that they treated each one, afterwards, with care and reverence. He never came to understand their language, nor they his, but they listened to him, they bowed to him, they followed him, they waited on him, they gave him a place next to the king, nodding to him as though he were a mute. And to please them he went on trying to remember more tracks, till the end of his days, forgetting even so, getting the order wrong, forgetting more and more, and supplying it as best he could, from mere habit.

But he never tried to tell them where the cave was. No one ever knew. No one even knew what mountain it was on.

Hitler and Bonhoeffer

James Martin

Pastor Bonhoeffer Becomes Engaged

Friend, I must tell you that she has entered my heart
   Like a bullet. During evening worship I find
My last prayers traveling without shame to a white
   House in Pätzig; I am still dreaming at curfew!
Her mother is torn by this, and I am great at
   Persuasion, but my future is uncertain now . . .

"Maria, I write after four weeks in this cell
They have given me, better said, I was given *to*.
Stand firm. The reasons for my presence here are well
Beyond discussion. Have you got your trousseau packed,
Or do women *pack* such things? I have heard them call
This prison healthy because we are exercised
Each day. They will censor this, but I am not blind,
Dearest, my only sweat has been from a cramped
                                                     leg."

In Hitler's Notebook, 1918

1.   Could Germans fear a Hütler or Heidler?
     A woman's trinket.
     Someone dreamt a wolf in me.

2.   Father was a stunning, drooling man, a post-man,
     and I am called the "weak" one,
               the bohemian son!

3.   I have found in the presence of true power
     women (will) laugh.

4   I saw I was to learn
         from their incompetence
         the importance of sheer *speaking*.
             That speeches could tear the cloth
             of Goethe's sleep.

5.   I will not close a corpse's mouth.

6.   Each bed was heaving. The barracks under blankets
         spitting vomit on each of his fourteen "Points."
         Submit! I turned in the years.
         I told them, that night, I would take up
         political work.

"Your Führer is not AntiChrist..."

> *"Why so hard?" the charcoal once said
> to the diamond; "for are we not close
> relations?"* —Nietzsche

PASTOR: I have no proof the difference
             Is more than pills, or facial hair,
             His peptic voice, the olid trance:

             The German brain that keeps me here
             Is not insane. Is not insane
             Or sane as mine which keeps me here.

             (But who has thought he is insane?)
             Or finally seen no difference
             In children held to kiss this man

             And folly kissed? This man has sense.
             And soldier, I should kiss this man,
             And that has made the difference.

SOLDIER: You are his Christ in *Todesbanden:*
             His Pastor of the Chains. It has
             Been said you turn your bath to wine;

             He keeps you here in hopes of this.
             But *this,* is not a Christian jest,
             Or schoolroom joke, and never was.

             Pastor, need I speak the rest?
             You cannot wash your hands with wine,
             Or wish to murder him who blessed

             The church you met to burn us in.

I accuse you
Who are Jews of "free" confession.

PASTOR: I have no God to flex for you.
Your Führer is not the AntiChrist
Who, shall I say, has more to do—

Was Goethe's greatest sin at last,
Unfaithfulness? A battered wife?
Are sins of the sons uncursed?

We treat our fear of God in life
As secret wisdom. What shall we say
Then to those who fear *men?* And if

You ever preach of this, or me,
I would advise, Jeremiah,
Chapter 31, verse 3.

A War Quartet, 1944

1.   R. Hess

The broken knife of Germany.
Its wound and target soaring. Fly,
From the heart of the heart of this country,
And then fly on, and again, fly.

2.   M. Bormann

Inside, inside. The pants and shirts
Of royalty, of Germany.
The toad undressing life in spurts,
The worm is bitter constantly.

3.   H. Himmler

We found ice in your chest. No veins
For blood to return from the skin.
A massive pile of unused coins
Whose faces, lying from the sun . . .

4.   H. Göring

Go, little heart. Envoy, coda
Of Nembutal. In the last crying
Limousine, the Meisterkiller,
Fat harridan, sits death draining.

Unsigned, In Eva Braun's Dress

I
Ordered Hess
To dine with me, bland,
Or burn himself.
He fell or flew.
I walked in on Goebbels
Who was shooting his sons.
I opened slow Göring's
Steel needlebox,
Unplugged the past, drugged and obese.
Soul, come back.
I sang
Or slept with Eva.
I offered to Speer
My plans for Berlin:
He offered to me
His plans for a book,
And a photograph
With me at the rear.
I would trade a plane for silence here.
Eva Braun is typing my will.
I leave:
    The stalled German Sea.
    Eva's dresses.
    Four trains without engines.
    One photograph.
And, as I sign this,
They are burning
My arms in a ditch
    of limbs and roots.

The Marriage of A. Hitler

Father Wagner, did you bring the kerosene?
Shall we call you Pastor, or let that drop?
I am your man. Miss Braun, of course, has seen
To that. We have the Psalms in French or Greek
As Testaments. Now I shall stand unseen
Behind; let *her* shine through. And then a cake
When this is done. Bormann is our bridesmaid.
A wedding trip? My room will do. A drink,

Or pills, and sleep. Miss Braun will dream she died
My wife, and then her dream will die. Without her,
How quickly life would cough me up. My bed
Shall be our state. No German hoped for war
This year, he hoped for wives; whose wives now hope
Him dead.
                    My dear, you are a Braun no longer.
I do.
Yes, I do.

Pastor Bonhoeffer's Last Prayer,
On the Importance of Illusion

                    Is unfinished.
It contains too much that is wise and good,
                    Unfinished, unfinished.
"I have just now finished Dostoyevsky's
Memoirs from the House of the Dead.

                    It holds a great
Deal that is wise and good. I am thinking
                    About his assertion
That man cannot live without hope." The world
Is unfinished and hope follows

                    Your illusion.
He knew that. He knew that illusion moved
                    Germans, before hope moved
Illusion. *Re*moved it. "The danger here
Never lasts more than a few minutes."

                    And we see him,
At least I see him, in the cell's air, tears
                    Welling, more slowly than
A tear wells loving us, his face so red
And welled, tears like string in his eyes,

                    Gasping for air,
More air, like ink, into his life. Because
                    He has kept on writing.
All of this time, kept on writing about
The tear on my cheek, rolling.

Having It Both Ways

A Conversation between
John Barth AND Joe David Bellamy

I N THE AIR-TERMINAL LOBBY *in Williamsport he was already seated, waiting. Standing up, he was taller than I expected, tougher and ruddier, more loose-jointed and lean through the belly. Still, he was unmistakably John Barth—I realized how my expectations had been skewed by black and white dust-jacket photos. Except for the corduroy and wide tie, he might have been a brigadier general in the RAF or a balding reincarnation of Sam Clemens with that sense of gravity and barely suppressed joviality and reddish-brown flyaway hair. His conversation was brisk, engaging, and pleasantly articulated in a "Piedmont accent," which, like the place of his birth, Cambridge, Maryland, seems almost-but-not-quite Southern.*

The occasion for the interview that came about that afternoon was Barth's excursion into Pennsylvania for a symposium date at the 1971 meeting of the Northeast Modern Language Association in Philadelphia and a sandwiched-in appearance at Mansfield State College, where he would read from one of his latest works, a novella entitled Perseid—*part of a group of novellas he was completing using various mythic stories.*

During the interview, conducted in Mansfield following his reading, Barth sipped from a glass of Löwenbräu and never appeared to tire. His processes of thought and expression took off in sustained leaps without the usual gaps, pauses, and short dribbles that characterize most people's mental activity.

"There is an interesting balance," Barth remarked at one

point, "between theorizing about what you're doing and
doing it. As you compose, particularly if you have a theoretical turn of mind, you're likely to be interested in working out any theoretical notions that you might be afflicted
with about the medium you're working in. But you also
know . . . that you work to a large degree by hunch and
intuition, and inspiration, as they say. Then, retrospectively,
you may understand a great deal more in the theoretical
way about what it was that you in fact did, than you understood at the time. When we talk about it, we're talking
retrospectively, so I think sometimes we give the impression
that we're all terribly theoretical when we sit down at the
desk, which of course we aren't."

Such qualifications notwithstanding, John Barth is nota-
ble, among other reasons, for the theoretical sophistication
of his work. In meeting him and talking to him, one quickly
begins to appreciate why this is so.

JOE DAVID BELLAMY: What sort of general ideas do
you have about the nature of change in contemporary
fiction writing at this point in history?

JOHN BARTH: History is more or less real, and so there
are more or less real reasons why the arts of the twentieth century don't much resemble those of the nineteenth, the nineteenth the eighteenth, the eighteenth the
seventeenth, and so forth. On the other hand, having
written fiction for a couple of decades, I'm impressed
more all the time by what seems to me the inescapable
fact that literature—because it's made of the common
stuff of language—seems more refractory to change in
general than the other arts. I think this is true most
specifically of prose fiction, probably because of its
historical roots in the popular culture. Tchaikovsky
would have a great deal of difficulty digging John Cage
or any other serious composers since the First World
War—much more trouble than Dostoyevsky would have
understanding Saul Bellow or even, for that matter,
Nabokov. Dostoyevsky would have trouble understanding *Finnegans Wake,* but then we who come after Joyce
do, too. Works like *Finnegans Wake* strike some of us
as being, after all, the monumental last cry of a certain

variety of modernism and not terribly *consequential*, though impressive in themselves.

The permanent changes in fiction from generation to generation more often have been, and are more likely to be, modifications of sensibility and attitude rather than dramatic innovations in form and technique. Especially in the United States novel, in our century, the landmark works, the landmark writers—I use that adjective deliberately because one distinguishes sometimes between what's excellent and what's historically important—the landmark writers more often than not are not formally or technically innovative. Fitzgerald, Hemingway the novelist, Joe Heller, Ralph Ellison, Phil Roth, Saul Bellow, John Updike—however much we may admire them on some sort of grounds, we don't particularly admire them for dramatic innovations in form and technique. I have to add immediately that these are not my *very* favorite writers; and those who are—Borges, Beckett, and Nabokov, among the living grand masters (and writers like Italo Calvino, Robbe-Grillet, John Hawkes, William Gass, Donald Barthelme)—*have* experimented with form and technique and even with the *means* of fiction, working with graphics and tapes and things, echoing a kind of experimentation that has been going on since the beginning of the century and harks back to such works as *Tristram Shandy*.

But even among these, it seems to me, the important difference from their predecessors is more a matter of sensibility and attitude than of means. What the writers that I just mentioned share (except Robbe-Grillet) is a more or less fantastical, or as Borges would say, "irrealist," view of reality; and this irrealism—not antirealism or unrealism, but irrealism—is all that I would confidently predict is likely to characterize the prose fiction of the 1970's. I welcome this (if it turns out to be, as a matter of fact, true), because unlike those critics who regard realism as what literature has been aiming at all along, I tend to regard it as a kind of aberration in the history of literature.

BELLAMY: What possible directions—of a formal or technical nature—do you see contemporary fiction going in?

BARTH: It's going in all directions, including what might appear to be certain retrograde directions. One sees, on the one hand, genuine experiments: concrete fiction, for example—the attempt to devise a narrative equivalent to concrete poetry. I've seen some striking examples of that, and of various kinds of three-dimensional fiction, action fiction, experiments with tapes, graphics, and the like.

On the other hand, just as painting in a certain period of history defines itself against still photography, so it may be that the particular aspects of literature that can't be duplicated in any other medium (especially the cinema), such as its linearity, for example, and its visual verbality, and its translation of all sense-stimuli into signs, are precisely the ones that we should pay the most attention to. That is, instead of trying to defeat time, for example, successive time, in narrative, as some writers have attempted in the twentieth century, perhaps we should *accept* the fact that writing and reading are essentially linear activities and devote our attention as writers to those aspects of experience that can best be rendered linearly—with words that go left to right across the page; subjects, verbs, and objects; punctuation!—instead of trying to force the medium into things that are not congenial to it. I say this with all sorts of reservations, because I *am* interested in formal experimentation.

The trick, I guess, in any of the arts at this hour of the world, is to have it both ways. That is, one more or less understands why the history of art, including the art of fiction, has led it through certain kinds of stages and phases to where we are now, and one does ill to deny that history or pretend that it hasn't happened. That's like pretending that the eighteenth century, nineteenth century, and early twentieth century didn't happen.

At the same time, just as one might come to the conclusion that to be linear is not necessarily to be wicked, one may appreciate that because an idea originates in the nineteenth century or eighteenth century, it is not necessarily a vicious idea in the twentieth century. And so if I were a composer, for example, I would try to find a way to be absolutely contemporary, insofar as my musical means are concerned—to address myself to the whole history of twentieth-century music, as well as the centuries preceding—and yet write beautiful melodies. (I don't like very much contemporary music as well as I like eighteenth- and nineteenth-century music. I can study it and find it interesting, but it doesn't move me very deeply.) If I were a painter in 1972, I would try to find some way to assimilate all the historical reasons that produce Frank Stella, let's say, and at the same time paint nudes, because one loves nudes.

Now the equivalent of that in fiction would be to find a way to assimilate what's gone before us in the twentieth century—Joyce, Beckett, Borges, and the rest —and yet tell stories, which is an agreeable thing to do. So, if one takes that to be the problem—how to have it both ways—then I think one can see why it is that fiction goes off in our time in some of the directions in which it's going.

BELLAMY: In the mid-sixties Louis D. Rubin wrote an article for the *Kenyon Review* called "The Curious Death of the Novel," in which he talked about the literary climate at that time. He said that the reason the novel was "dead" was that all the great novelists had died, and the critics believed that *those* were "the modern novelists." Since those particular writers had died, the critics thought the novel was dead, too. Rubin ended up saying *he* didn't think the novel was dead at all, of course.

One observation he made about you—you may have read it (this was after *The Sot-Weed Factor*)—was that you had gone back and explored the eighteenth-century novel, taking it as far as it can go. But then, an implication of his praise was that favorite old saw of American criticism: now we are waiting for the big book [*laughter from Barth*]. What was the motivation behind *The Sot-Weed Factor?* Do you think *Giles Goat-Boy,* being as it seemed to be yet another new direction for you—a movement toward greater irrealism—might possibly have been the sort of book Rubin was asking for? And then, how do these books figure generally in the death-of-the-novel controversy?

BARTH: Well, the *Goat-Boy* may or may not be the one Rubin was looking for. It may or may not have been a successor to *The Sot-Weed Factor*. But it is true that one of the things you may be doing as you go through your bibliography, as when you go through your life, is following out certain lines of thought apart from what you're saying overtly.

Thomas Mann remarks that what a writer is writing *about* is seldom the main point; it's what he's doing with his left hand that really matters. *The Sot-Weed Factor* was composed, along with all the other reasons, with certain things in mind about the history of the novel, including the history of my own novels. My first two novels were very short and relatively realistic. By the time I began to compose *The Sot-Weed Factor*—apart from all my other motives and accidental reasons for being interested in that story, like the fact that I grew up near Cook's Point where the real Ebenezer Cook did have an estate—I was more acquainted with the history of literature than I'd been when I began to write fiction. And so I set about to untie my hands; I presumptuously felt them tied by the history of the genre and, less presumptuously, by the kinds of things that I myself had been writing before.

One thing I did was move from a merely comic mode to a variety of farce, which frees your hands even more than comedy does. But there was another impulse, which I understood better retrospectively—to sort of go to the roots of the novel and see whether I could bring back something new. The eighteenth-century literary conventions were appropriate in part because the eighteenth century and the seventeenth were the centuries when the part of the world that I was writing about became established in European history and imagination. The theme of European innocents coming into America and the theme of the virgin poet—who is not really a poet as long as he is innocent, and who becomes one when he loses his innocence—were congenial.

But the possibility of constructing a fantastically baroque plot appealed to me most: the idea of turning vigorously against the modernist notion that plot is an anachronistic element in contemporary fiction. I've never found that a congenial notion; it seemed to me that there were ways to be quite contemporary and yet go at the art in a fashion that would allow you to tell complicated stories simply for the aesthetic pleasure of complexity, of complication and unravelment, suspense, and the rest. I don't think you could do it with a long face: you would almost have to be parodying the genre in some respect to bring it off. But I don't believe that that is necessarily a sterile or unproductive thing to do. I don't think that it is a particular sign of decadence, especially in the novel, because (as Leslie Fiedler is fond of saying) the novel has always been dying. It was "dying" from the time it was conceived, and it begins in parody. Not just with Fielding, whom I was parodying to some extent—I mean Fielding parodying Richardson—but with Cervantes parodying the chivalric romances. The first novels that we have are already parodies of things in the literary tradition; the mode seems congenial to the genre.

BELLAMY: So you are not pessimistic about the waning of the novel? You wouldn't advise all young writers to go out and become filmmakers?

BARTH: When I see a young man taking up the practice of fiction as a vocation in this age of the camera, it seems to me that he is doing a very quixotic thing to dedicate his mortal time to that possibly dead art form. But what better adjective! If it is a "quixotic" thing to do, then he's right where the genre begins! So while one writes fiction now in a sort of apocalyptic ambience, it doesn't finally matter at all to the art of literature whether historically this particular little genre fades away. After all, literature got along very well without the novel for most of its history. It comes into existence at a particular time because of particular social and technological conditions; if they no longer obtain and the novel as we know it passes out of literary history—there is no great tragedy for anybody. It doesn't mean the end of narrative literature, certainly. It certainly doesn't mean the end of storytelling. The cinema can do some things *like* the novel, but in language, in words, one can do things one can't do in the cinema. And one can do them in ways that have very little to do with the classical novel.

BELLAMY: This begins to sound like a convincing *raison d'être* for your experiments in *Lost in the Funhouse*. How is it that you turned to "Fiction for Print, Tape, Live Voice" and your continuing preoccupation with myth?

BARTH: It's that aforementioned impulse to investigate the roots that has led some of us in the last few years to explore the possibilities of electronic tapes. That's a way of having it both ways. In some aspects, tapes get us back to the oral tradition out of which literature comes. You have the authorial voice, after all, telling the stories when you work on tape. On the other hand, unlike purely oral literature, a tape has some of the virtues of print: it's interruptable and referable. You can stop a tape, as you can't stop a live storyteller; and you can go back to a particular point—two things that you *can* do on the page that you can't do in the movie theater, for example, and that you couldn't do with the live oral tradition very easily.

And the same impulse—to find ways to have it both ways—has led some of us too to deal with received stories, particularly the myths. I always felt that it was a bad idea on the face of it, though there are beautiful counter-examples, to write a more or less realistic piece of fiction, one dimension of which keeps pointing to the classical myths—like John Updike's *Centaur,* or Joyce's *Ulysses,* or Malamud's *The Natural.* Much as one may admire those novels in other respects, their authors have hold of the wrong end of the mythopoeic stick. The myths themselves are produced by the collective narrative imagination (or whatever), partly to point down at our daily reality; and so to write about our daily experiences in order to point up to the myths seems to me mythopoeically retrograde. I think it's a more interesting thing to do, if you find yourself preoccupied with mythic archetypes or what have you, to address them directly.

BELLAMY: That's certainly what you seem to be doing to the *Perseid*. How does that work exactly?

BARTH: Well, for example, when I felt at one point in my tape experiments that after all there's something narcissistic about this business of exploiting the authorial voice—my response was to write a story about the myth of Narcissus and Echo, instead of writing a realistic story that echoes narcissism. At the same time, I made the story into a metaphor for the condition of working with tapes.

Echo in the classical myth begins as a girl with a body and her own voice, who can say what she wants to. She's a storyteller, and Zeus hires her to tell stories to his wife, Hera; to distract her with fiction so that he can slip out and make love to other women. Echo does this, and Hera punishes her by taking away her ability to say what she wants to say: she can only repeat the words of others, but she still does it in her own voice, and she still has a body. When she falls in love with Narcissus and her love is not requited, she pines away (we're told in the original myth) until she has no more physical presence at all. She becomes only a voice, her voice, echoing what other people say.

Now in my story, called "Echo," she has passed through one more stage of refinement so that she's lost her individual voice, with its own timbre and inflection, and she has no body any more. She only repeats what others say, in their own voices—which is what a tape machine does. Echo, at that point, becomes a kind of proto-Ampex. Now the idea was to devise a story about Echo and Narcissus and Tiresias the prophet—who is involved in this myth, too, and who can see backwards and forwards in time—the plot of which would be arranged such that it would be impossible to say, listening to the story on the tape, whether it's Echo telling the story in Tiresias' voice, for example, or in Narcissus' voice, or whether Narcissus is telling the story about Echo, et cetera. Finally, of course, it's the *author's* voice you're hearing, and the author is always all of those things he makes up, so the metaphor becomes rigorously applicable to the conditions of the fiction. Do you understand what I mean?

BELLAMY: Yes. In fact, it strikes me that this is a complex version of the kind of story—and there are a lot of these now by a lot of writers—which tends to start talking about the formal nature of the story and the process of its composition.

BARTH: Exactly. The process is the content, more or less.

BELLAMY: I'm thinking of other examples in *Lost in the Funhouse* which do that in different ways. Do you think there's a basic conflict between that kind of anti-illusionistic writing and the storytelling impulse? That is, when you start talking about the equipment of the story and deliberately break the illusion of the story, do you possibly disrupt the impulse you have toward storytelling and forgo those qualities?

BARTH: No, I don't think there's a conflict, only a kind of tension, which can be used. When we talk about it this way it all sounds dreadfully self-conscious, involuted, vertiginous, dull. In the actual execution it doesn't have to be that at all; it can be charming, entertaining; it can even be illusionist. And it's an ancient idea. It's as old as Greek drama, anyhow—to play on the fact that this is a play that you're watching. And Shakespeare does it constantly: "All the world's a stage," et cetera. *The Tempest* is the example *par excellence:* the master of illusion uncloaking his illusions on one level while maintaining them on another.

In other words, the anti-illusionist aspect can be part of the prestidigitation. And that's not decadence or mere gimmickry: it's a way of getting certain kinds of things expressed. Borges makes the remark that those moments in literature when the characters within a work begin to comment on, or be aware of, the fiction that they're in, disturb us because such moments remind us of the fiction that *we're* in. A Schopenhauerian idea, which seems to me to be unexceptionable.

The trick, always, is to be at the same time entertaining. I still regard literature as a form of pleasure;

and while there are lots of pleasures, including the pleasure of vertigo, I myself like a kind of fiction that, if it's going to be self-conscious, is at least comic about its own self-consciousness. Otherwise, self-consciousness can be a bloody bore. What is more loathsome than the self-loathing of a self one loathes?

BELLAMY: Getting back to the subject of myth, I would be interested in your response to this passage from Robert Scholes' book, *The Fabulators*: "Some influential critics have been ready to proclaim a new age of myth as the most likely literary development of the immediate future. But this, it seems to me, is the least likely of literary developments. [*Barth is laughing.*] Once so much is known *about* myths and archetypes, they can no longer be used innocently. Even their connection to the unconscious finally becomes attenuated as the mythic materials are used more consciously. All symbols become allegorical to the extent that we understand them. Thus the really perceptive writer is not merely conscious that he is using mythic materials: He is conscious that he is using them consciously. He *knows,* finally, that he is allegorizing. Such a writer, aware of the nature of categories, is not likely to believe that his own mythic lenses really capture the truth. Thus the use of myth will inevitably partake of the comic."

BARTH: That seems to me to be simply the truth.

BELLAMY: Right. Then he goes on and says finally: that the modern writer's predicament is that he "knows too much." And this is precisely what keeps his perspective from being seriously mythic.

BARTH: I see his point. I'm not quite sure I agree with it, except as a description of the problem and of the *likely* results. It certainly explains why most of the pieces of literature which resort directly to mythic materials, classical mythic materials, and are at the same time moving and touching and effective for us, tend to be comic, or satiric, or parodic literature. This doesn't necessarily mean however that they're not passionate or impassioned, in the same way as *Don Quixote*, which begins as a parody of a certain literary genre but soon transcends all that. What Scholes says doesn't rule out the genuinely mythopoeic; it only puts it underground and makes it come in in other places.

Certainly the problem of knowing too much, in the sense in which Scholes speaks of it here, is real. One remembers how writers of the early twentieth century reacted to their awareness of that problem: those writer-figures in Thomas Mann, for example, who reach a point where they decide they don't want to understand any more about what they're doing; they turn their back on knowledge in order to keep producing: a kind of counter-Faustian notion. Everybody who writes stories and poems, if he happens to have read a few things as well, confronts this problem: the danger of understanding too much about what he's up to. It's like the problem of being perfectly psychoanalyzed. Many artists resist that kind of understanding of themselves, lest it hamper their progress. We know that the things that lead us to get our work done are most imperfectly understood at best, and perhaps had better be left alone, lest tinkering with the machinery, or even looking at it too closely, impede its operation.

But it would be foolish to imagine that the collective mythopoeic energy, if one can use that term, is greater or less from one generation, or from one century, to another. I think it simply has to take different forms. And some kind of writers have it, and others don't, regardless of their other merits and demerits. Henry James is not a very mythopoeic writer. Dickens is a tremendously mythopoeic writer. Of course, when you consciously use an old myth, a received myth, like the myth of Perseus, or the myth of Helen, Paris, and Mene-laus, then whatever there is of the originally mythopoeic in your own imagination is either going to come in some-where else in that text—with new characters, or lan-guage, or new twists to the old myth, or else will simply flow in to fill in those mythic receptacles which go by the names of Paris, Menelaus, Helen. I believe firmly, in other words, that some of the serious affect that we experience in the face of genuine myth can be experi-enced in the face of contemporary "comic" fiction using mythic materials.

BELLAMY: Would you say that contemporary writers are ever able to create their own myths? Or would you say that it's *possible* to create myths?

BARTH: It's a presumptuous thing to aspire to, perhaps—to really make a new myth. And I don't know very much about the scholarly discipline of mythology. But some literary critics and students of myth—Philip Young, for example—will classify, upon occasion, certain works of individual authors, like Irving's *Rip Van Winkle,* as genuine myth. Occasionally it happens! My colleague and friend at Buffalo, Leslie Fiedler, has written a great deal on the subject of the element of the mythopoeic in individual authors, particularly American. I find the things he says on this subject very impressive.

Now a novel like *Giles Goat-Boy,* on the other hand, is not in any sense an attempt to make up a new myth. Not at all, you know. That's a novel that illustrates what Scholes was talking about. When I wrote *The Sot-Weed Factor* I wasn't as aware of certain mythic patterns as I was made aware of them consequently, or subsequently, by the reaction of certain critics and reviewers and students who knew more about comparative mythology than I did. Once one is made aware of the patterns, then the problem is how to be conscious of what one's doing, which can be a fruitful thing, without being in an inhibitory way *self*-conscious about what one's doing—in other words, to avoid being paralyzed by your own knowledge. What I did in the case of the *Goat-Boy* novel was to try to abstract the patterns, and then write a novel which would consciously, even self-consciously, follow the patterns, parody the patterns, satirize the patterns, but with good luck transcend the satire a little bit in order to say some of the serious things I had in mind to say. Otherwise it would be a farce, a great trifle —which, of course, some readers found it to be. But the intention was to escalate the farce, to escalate the parody, until the thing took on a genuine dramatic dimension of its own. This may not be making up a new myth, but it's getting to a dimension of response that we can associate with myth, through a comical and farcical mode.

BELLAMY: You said in a previous interview that, "There are deep metaphysical reasons why we need more Fielding-like books today with plots where everybody turns out to be related to everybody else. . . ."

BARTH: Did I say that?

BELLAMY: Maybe you were writing *The Sot-Weed Factor* when you said that.

BARTH: Or probably I had just written it and needed to justify it to my own imagination [*laughs*]. I can't even remember making that comment. . . . But I spoke already of the business of plot as a rather exact equivalent of the element of melody in music. And I like plot in fiction in the same way that I like melodic music. The history of melody—how could you say that—the Dun and Bradstreet rating of the element of melody in music parallels very carefully the Dun and Bradstreet rating of the element of plot in fiction. Plot goes out of fashion at the same time that melody goes out of fashion. And melody may come back into music by the back door— popular music taken seriously by non-popular musicians and composers. And story may get back into fiction by that same kind of door. The kids are all turned on by science fiction now, which, whatever else it is, is usually very tight in plot.

BELLAMY: How do you come to terms with the arguments made by Robbe-Grillet, and Nathalie Sarraute, and others, that such elements as plot, character, omniscience, and so on, are obsolete notions based on metaphysical assumptions that are no longer applicable?

BARTH: One could say, of course, that the complicated plot in which everything works out and resolves itself in the end belongs historically to centuries where, not necessarily the writer, but the writer's audience, more or less believed in some kind of destiny or fate that saw that things worked out. In other words, periods when one could take a dramatistical view of one's own life— where one's fortunes followed from one's character, and one's relations worked out more or less appropriately, as they should. You could say that the age of the plotted novel belongs to the age when people took that more seriously than they can take it in the twentieth century.

Agreeing with all that, I'd still say that if you reject
these devices on those grounds, you're operating from
an absolutely realist argument. It would be the premises
of realism, in other words, that would object to a literary
convention for those reasons. Do you follow me? One
can think of a lot of twentieth-century French fiction,
for example, as being a more subtle kind of realism:
instead of being social realism, or psychological realism,
the fiction of Robbe-Grillet or Nathalie Sarraute is a
kind of epistemological realism. It's the processes of
consciousness that are being duplicated, a higher and
hi-er fi to the processes of knowing and perception,
achieved with more and more sophisticated literary
woofers and tweeters.

But another way to address that state of affairs is to
regard fiction as artifice in the first place. And if you
acknowledge and embrace the artificial aspect of art,
which you can't get rid of anyway, then it doesn't necessarily follow, for example, that you have to abandon
certain kinds of literary devices simply because they're
metaphors for notions that are no longer viable. If you
are working in the comic mode, you may be free *ipso
facto* to make use of all sorts of conventions because
you're parodying them. Your tracks are covered as far
as the Robbe-Grillet argument is concerned, and at
the same time you can exploit the outmoded conventions for all they're worth to get certain things
done that you just can't get done in any other way.
. . . Certainly it's true that a plotted novel is rigorously
unrealistic.

BELLAMY: How would that argument go using an example from character as well as plot?

BARTH: One of Robbe-Grillet's points, which I believe he
borrows from Roland Barthes, is that the novel of character, such as *Madame Bovary,* for example, or Tolstoy's
work, belongs to the *age* of character, to the age of
the individual. And in mass society, for example, when
individualism as a philosophy is historically discredited,
the novel of character is a kind of anachronism. I find
that to be a most persuasive argument, but I note to
myself that, for example, the simple device of telling a

story in the first person obviates almost all those objections.

What I mean is that you and I still imagine ourselves to be characters, and our lives are influenced by other people around us whom we see as characters and our relations to whom we perceive in a dramatic, in a dramatical, way. As individuals we still live in calendar and clock time; and no matter how that time may be discredited by physicists, it's nevertheless the kind of time we live in during most of our waking experiences. "Microscopes and telescopes," Goethe says simply, "distort the natural focus of our eyes." The metaphysics of cause and effect, for example, may be extremely debatable. But the fact is that we live our lives most of the time with a very simple, crude, and perhaps old-fashioned understanding of cause and effect. We *have* to.

Now, if you write a novel with an "I" narrator, none of these things that Robbe-Grillet objects to as being obsolete or anachronistic can be charged against the *author,* because they only reflect the anachronistic presuppositions of a first-person narrator, who is no more responsible for them than the rest of us are as we go through our lives. So such a simple device as working in the first person, such a simple premise as the comic mode, or the parodic mode, or a fantastical mode, rather than a realistic mode, already, it seems to me, unties you, sets you free from some of these objections—which otherwise are quite compelling.

BELLAMY: One last question. In your essay on Borges called "The Literature of Exhaustion," you said *The Sot-Weed Factor* or *Giles Goat-Boy* are novels which "imitate the form of the Novel by an author who imitates the role of Author." What did you mean by that?

BARTH: I mean that's strictly correct. One of the interesting things about eighteenth-century fiction, about the early novel, is that the author with a capital "A," that fellow who intrudes . . .

BELLAMY: Oh, *that* author. You don't mean *you* as an author.

BARTH: Yes, I don't mean that I'm presuming to a medium that I have no business mucking around in [*laughter*]. Though there are not wanting people who say that that's the case too.

We have such a long history, in the history of fiction, of novels that pretend to be anything but novels. The novels starts that way. *Don Quixote* pretends to be an historical record translated by the Cid Hamete Benengeli, and Richardson's novels pretend to be the letters of Pamela or Clarissa. Fielding's novels pretend to be this, that, or the other thing—anything except that it should be a piece of *fiction!* And in the modern tradition we have novels masking as everything: novels masking as diaries; novels, like that beautiful one of Nabokov's, *Pale Fire,* pretending to be a poem with pedantic footnotes, and so on.

I thought it might be interesting to write a novel which simply imitates the form of the novel, rather than imitating all these other kinds of documents. In other words, it pretends to be a piece of fiction.

The Gate at the Throat

Stewart Lindh

DID Chinese ancients leave their villages
at dawn in rowboats carrying wicker
baskets inside which was movement?
Did yellow stalks of arms row the boats

across water, water and stop
where the oars were dropped
and drawn inside the boats to rest?
Was a basket opened, a dark bird taken

out and from a pocket a gold ring
slipped over the neck to slide
down the feathers and wait?
Was a long bamboo string tied

to the gold ring and the bird released
to sail over the water, no weight
on the ring, no tug
of the string on its breath?

Was a shadow seen swimming below,
itself with many others? Did the bird
waver, lunge, and emerge carrying
in its beak a fish?

Then did the universe try to swallow
and puzzle and puzzle until the string
tugged, the ring turned to steel,
and the meaning rowed near?

The Green Tree

James Reiss

Ever since my daughters started to walk,
I have had increasing difficulty with my eyes.
I remember the day Wendy took her first steps, when
she said "bamboo" and waddled over to pat the rusty
  bumper

of a truck, I could barely make out the writing
scrawled in dirt on the trailer and had trouble focusing
as she stepped into its shadow.
The morning in Maine when she raced down the beach

and splashed into the ocean before I could reach her,
I actually mistook her for another little girl in pink
whom—I am sorry to say—I began leading slowly out of the
  water.
Then there is Jill: when she first walked I remember

looking at her and thinking, "I am a camera fading back,
  back."
Years later when she would go rollerskating with Wendy,
my eyes were so bad I could no longer tell
where the sidewalks left off and my daughters began.

By now everything has faded into fine print. I
have been to a doctor who says he is also troubled,
but has sons. My only son died three days after
birth, weighing two pounds. His name was

Jeffrey, but I have always preferred to call him "Under-
  the-Earth"
or, especially on rainy days, "Under-the-Sod." In fact,
sometimes I catch myself repeating these words: "My only
  son,
Under-the-Sod, is playing over there by the green tree."

The Bridled Ass

William Mathes

> The end of our race is death; 'tis the
> necessary object of our aim, which if it fright
> us, how is it possible to advance a step with-
> out a fit of ague? The remedy the vulgar
> use is not to think on't; but from what
> brutish stupidity can they derive so gross a
> blindness? They must bridle the ass by the
> tail. . . .
>
> We trouble life by the care of death, and
> death by the care of life; the one torments,
> the other frights us.
>
> —Montaigne

Because of his great strength, his unpredictable ways, and his obscure origins; because he had learned to make fire so quickly, so easily, as though it sparked from his fingertips effortlessly; because he had always been apart and excellent; because he was without fear; because he was the best hunter—he was given the name "of the fire," or "like the fire," or "voice of the fire." Before entering the company of men, he had been tested, but he had turned his test into a test for them; he had amazed them and made them ashamed, then and always.

He was sent alone into the forest to survive and hunt, to bring back a major kill. He came back with a bear, a great red bear, taller than himself, as red as the smoky fires. He came back at night, walking into the firelight with the bear walking behind him. He had tamed it, not killed it. In less than the time he had been given to kill, he had tamed. After that they called him Fire, because on that night he had made the great red bear dance in front of their fires. Many were afraid, and the elders were suspicious.

Years passed; he lived and grew. Each day the bear waited for him at the edge of the forest, and when he left to hunt, it was seen following him, running behind him, hunting with him. And when Fire took a woman, the bear mated; some said the cubs of the red bear played with the children of Fire. Some said that Fire was a beast, to be feared and respected, an animal-god that only seemed to be a man. And at night sitting around their fires, listening to Fire speak, listening to his stories of the hunt, some said they saw animal light in his eyes, others said they saw the fire itself. And when no one could or would, he reflected on the order and disorder of things, he spoke of life and death.

Where there had been few questions, he found many; he saw god in everything. Their god was a beast living near them, unmolested, untouchable, immune—depending on the season and the beast's whim. Alone, never with another, it was indispensable, ghastly, beautiful beyond understanding. There were stories of larger beasts, greater gods in other places at other times, but confronting their own they could not believe anything but its commanding reality, its persistent, awesome presence. And not one of them had ever sought other realities, other gods.

In the summer they moved to temporary shelters on the slopes, following the game, but always with their winter home in view below in the valley. In the winter, they came down to the lowlands where the sun, though brittle and distant, remained warm even when there was snow on the ground. And the game followed them, and they followed their god—and it them—up and back, back and up. It had always been so.

He was the best hunter and the one to whom everyone looked for discovery and innovation, although he had no council seat—these being reserved for older and more conventional men. Still he was a power among them, the power of surprise and mystery which everyone responded to and which he earned by his exploits. Except for the red bear, he was always alone, always hunting or worshiping; the two were the same for him. The others were occupied in the same way, hunting and worshiping; but only Fire drew the bonds tightly between the two.

In all things he did, there was this going to the limits, taking the normal and accepted way and changing it, making something new of it, hounding it to a death of meanings. Some were angry with him because he could not leave anything alone. His innovations seemed to breed malice in others. And their malice made them strange to him. While often enraged, he was without malice. And so, strange to them and them to him, he was always alone.

He took a wife early, as was the custom, and she had given him five children, but they were still young—too young to worship or hunt. His wife stayed separate from him with the children, as was the custom. And so, he was estranged from her and she from him, though with mutual regard and regret. There were times, even later, when in spite of themselves and in spite of custom and common sense, he was able to know her and to feel her living center, know her as he knew himself and the great red bear. When he would touch her with his hands and his lips and she would wake as another person—the stranger of his stranger. They would hunt and worship each other's body, rolling and tossing and shaking the ground like gods coupling, throwing dust and destroying the order of the place. She loved and worshiped the demonic thing in him that turned the easy and conventional into the difficult and the holy— she participated in his loneliness and his terrible love of what was, of what she was, of the nape of existence, of the thrust of life, of the abyss of death.

His children basked in the glory of his prowess as a hunter. They watched him coming and going, and they romped with the cubs of the red bear. They met him with the game and helped him carry it back, and the oldest boy helped him dress it. There was no end to his comings and goings. He had enough to share with the others, and in the lean times it was he who led the expeditions around the rim of the valley as far as they dared to follow him, to search out the game—for the game searched for water and he knew all the watering places and knew their needs even as they knew them, even as he knew his own.

But their emergencies were rare and he was free to go alone, often hunting without killing, searching for the beast-god and stalking it—even though it was sacrilege to do so. He talked freely of it and was challenged once, but he explained his search as worship—how better to worship the god than to stay with it, to know its every move, its intimate nature, its delightful eccentricities? The elders were dismayed by his dreadful logic. At first he stalked the beast only when he had no need to hunt for food. But he became even more expert than before in finding and killing game, in providing for himself and his family, so that he brought back more each time than he needed and gave it to other families—to soften the anger at what he was doing.

WHEN THE OTHERS found that he was stalking their god, openly devoting himself to knowing their god, he was challenged by a fine but lesser man. They fought and he had had to cripple the man in order to remain free to stalk the god. Unwilling to injure, even to defend himself, he fought expertly but without lust. It was even more shocking to all who watched when he wept with the man he had crippled. But he had his way.

He asked for time to speak before the council of elders and was permitted to explain—and he was not challenged again. The elders and holy men saw how great was his power and how quickly he had crippled the challenger. They spoke of ill omens and of the evil the god would do them—and he promised to stop when the first evil omen appeared, for he was a believer too. It was just that he believed more than the others, and that he also loved more than the others. And when the council was over, he was free to do as he wished, without a peer, without a guide, the most dangerous man alive.

The food he gave freely pacified many, but the holy men mocked him behind his back. He knew of this, but it did not matter. Already estranged from them, he did not need their approval for what he thought or what he did, and their malice did not touch him, except to make him more eager to know the god and to make him sadder that he was only a man.

They rarely saw the beast-god and when they did, everyone prostrated themselves before it and the good omen was marked by feasting. Not long after Fire had crippled his challenger, a child saw the god high above the valley idling on the shelf of a ridge and, well trained, the child called the glad words and everyone saw and prostrated themselves, calling words of praise. But there was something different this time. They looked up at the ridge and saw the man, Fire—a respectful distance from the god, but there with it all the same, waiting quietly, patiently—not stalking as one stalks game, but simply being with it, being close to the god. And there were some in the crowd that thought to worship the man too, the relations between the two seemed so close and natural, even comfortable. They felt that the god permitted the man to come so near because of the man's prowess. Some watching hated the man because of his singular position and his courage. But Fire enraptured, did not hear their shouts because his heart was overflowing with praise, memorizing each detail of the god, loving the beast, becoming one with it in his mind, alone, silent, and more alive than those who worshiped from the valley below.

He returned during the feast, but no one questioned him. Now he was truly apart from them, even more than he had been before, and the holy men, with their special wisdom, were waiting for a sign, for an evil omen—perhaps wishing for a disaster, in this way to bring down the man and humble him before the god and themselves. They had faith—and their faith was in the malice of the god and in the certainty of their revenge.

The holy men, thinking to bend the importance of the feast away from Fire and toward themselves, honored him deviously. At the height of the celebration, they asked him to go with them to the painting caves, where he would be permitted to watch them perform their ritual paintings of the god-beast on the walls of the caves. This removed him from the center of attention and placed him in a humble position, waiting on them, watching them, holding their oil lamps. He was one of the few ever honored in this way.

He followed the holy men to the caves, following the flickering of their lamps, helping them carry the ritual pigments, watching and marveling at the visions in ochre the yellow light revealed. Squatting behind the holy men, Fire watched them perform the ritual, watched them carefully draw and paint again the same form, watched the god-beast's image emerge on the cave walls.

They stayed there several days, drawing, painting, chanting, fasting, allowing themselves only a few sips of the water they had brought with them, and after a while their visions came more clearly and their passion was finer. But not their paintings. The holy men had only one image and it was repeated over and over again, no matter how intense their visions.

His visions became clearer and finer too. Overcome by the beauty of the god-beast, Fire wanted the paintings to resemble the images in his mind, wanted the god-beast more richly worshiped. Forgetting himself, forgetting his position, he leaped to the cave wall, pushed the holy men aside, and began to draw his vision with one handful after another of flaming ochre and deadly black. He developed the small figures of their god into an image so huge that it could barely be seen in the span of a glance, and one so accurate and vivid that when he was finally finished and fell back to see what he had done, he trembled as though in its presence. The holy men held council while he worked, wondering what to do about his violation of their ritual, afraid to challenge him when he was so wild in his strange passion; then they returned to see what he had done, and saw him weeping openly, great silver tears of joy and exhaustion. The holy men turned to the wall flickering in the yellow light and saw the god-beast itself, there, captured on that wall, more real than a drawing could be, so real that they forgot their plotting, fell to their knees, and worshiped too, worshiped the overwhelming image Fire had created.

The holy men never told what had happened in the cave, and Fire was not inclined to make known his deep feelings. It was not what he had done that left its mark on him, but what he had felt. The passion of drawing the god had brought him even closer to it and fed his yearning to achieve some final and total intimacy. As the feasting drew to a close, he decided to try to ride the beast-god.

He realized the challenge to his abilities would be great and that it might take years to come close enough. But he had already done everything else a man can do, and he was still in his prime. He knew that there would be those who would want to stop him, that some of the holy men might curse him openly; to have him attempt such a thing would make all the people nervous, would keep their lives unsettled. And not only was the outcome in doubt, but the consequences were fearful to imagine, as much so if he succeeded as if he did not. So he would not tell anyone; as alone as before, he would prepare and persist, fortified by his faith that he and the beast-god were destined to know each other in a physical and total way.

After the feast there was always a great hunt to replenish the store of game, to be sun-dried and preserved. He led the hunt and it was so successful that everyone spoke well of him again and he was called, as he had been called before, "the one-who-hunts like fire." But still the holy men waited—not interfering, but not joining in the praise. And the "one-who-hunts like fire" felt he had completed a responsibility and was now free to begin to carry out his plan. At first, stalking only in the morning of the days he did not hunt, he gradually succeeded in finding and staying with the beast-god for longer periods into the day. Each time he came closer; each time the beast-god waited. The god seemed to make himself available to him, but there was also his own skill and his way of feeling and being what he stalked. And he knew no fatigue; even after a morning of hunting game, he would dash again into the forest and climb the heights searching again for it, devouring the plains and forests like a wild summer fire. The red bear gave up following him, went hunting alone.

He had been the first to swim, thinking that he might move through the water—after feeling its support bathing in the river, feeling the way it moved him around, the way his hands pushing it past his body moved his body. He had been the first to swim the river and back, and the others had learned from him, but he had broken the sacredness of the river and its inviolability. In the same way, now he dared with his body and used his strength for himself and gladly—unmindful of the risks and unhampered by any guilt of violating or diminishing the sacred: the truly sacred would take care of itself, no less, certainly, than he took care of himself.

He followed the beast-god into the dusk and watched where it slept, watched it all night from a respectful

distance, watched it stir in the morning's first light. And he
discovered that the beast-god often went along a certain
trail beneath an overhang, a lip of rock, sequestered by
nature. Improbable good fortune! Like men, the god had
habits—not as fixed, nor as comprehensible, but still habits.
The god passed by this ledge often at dusk on its way to
a thicket in a deep gorge, where it slept protected from
the weather and the prying eyes of men and other beasts.
And so it was in near darkness that Fire came to the ledge
and waited there one night, but the beast-god did not come;
another night, and still it did not come.

Back in the village everyone wondered what had become
of Fire; he had not returned during the two days as well
as the two nights, for he was resting for the night watch
and hunting a little for his own needs. The holy men
claimed he had been struck down by the beast, by their
god, and would not be seen again. His wife waited before
she grieved, and those so inclined recalled his life and
wondered about it. His children were sure he would return.
Enjoying the irony of his disappearance, making it an evil
omen, the holy men began to denounce him and had everyone looking for disaster.

On the third evening of the third cycle of the moon, at
dusk, the round hills bounding out of the flat valley like
storm clouds billowing, he waited, rested and strong, on the
ledge above the trail, the holy trail. The god-beast came
on slowly. He watched its golden flanks redden in the
sunset, the greens of the forest gray, and the browns
blacken. Above, the sky was open and the stars were convened. On such a night, anything might happen. The god-
beast stopped, looked over its shoulder at the setting sun,
moved on again—perhaps sensing him, perhaps bemused
by the slack time between dusk and darkness. The man
felt himself driven with love; his eyes filled with worship
and tears fell on his cheeks—the beauty of the god, the
fullness of life, the strength of his body, the knowledge
that would be his, the horror of time passing.

The tears fell down his cheeks and he dropped onto
the back of the god-beast and wrapped his arms around
its neck. There was a moment falling free in space, a
moment when he hit the rough hide, then a moment he had

dreamed of and planned for, when the beast was shocked into statuesque immobility, shocked into mortality. They were frozen together in conflicting realities, the man crouched flat on its back, the god-beast in terror at being suddenly mounted and violated, at being known. A beginning in mutual shock and terror, the abyss bridged, and the security of innocence lost.

Down the darkness now, and down into it ran the beast with the man clinging to it. Pressed to it, grasping its revolving flanks, grasping flesh and fur, and holding its sides with his legs, already aching from the strange stance; he felt its bones move in their joints and he knew the slap of flesh and the twist of muscle, a god's flesh, a god's muscle. No man had ever known such love, such terror—and they went, clinging and running into the darkness, out into and through the forests and over the valley rim onto the plain beyond. And as they went he felt and then heard the beast's great heart pumping under him, and it was in their hearts—his beating with the beast's—that they were consumed together, in their terror and in their love: the beast's love of self and love of freedom being lost, and the man's love of the unknown being satisfied.

Without slowing, the beast ran on, shaking the man, trying to toss him off, but the man persisted. The plain was limitless—they crashed through the streams, trampled down the tall grass, opened paths in the places beyond paths. The beast gradually turned in a slow arc and headed back from where they had come. The man could not see—the grass splayed out under him like waves and he caught glimpses of it as they pushed on, and the streams were merely more of the same, but black and wet and cold for an instant. His arms ached and his legs were like straw bundles, but he was able to stay on all night and the beast ran all night with Fire on its back, consuming darkness, consuming the land, consuming each other.

The women making the campfires and the early hunters eating before they left saw them on the ridge. The silhouette of the beast coming on hard with the man breaking the evenness of its back, running the rim, the man moving with the beast as part of its body, the man and the beast embraced and terribly mortal in their resolve. The women and early hunters called out the name of their god, shouted for everyone to come and see—and some called out the name of the man, the man called Fire, the "one-who-hunts like fire," and everyone watched the beast now maddened with fatigue and terror, running directly toward the village. And seeing too late the crowd, unable to sustain that last terror, scattering men and women and children before it, it fell in full stride just beyond the village, its heart broken, blood gushing from its mouth; and the man fell with it, still clinging, still weeping, the new god, the man who had ridden the god to death, the man who had butchered immortality.

The man rolled off the carcass, exhausted, and watched the great heaving sides that were still moving, still in flight, kick stiffly into death. From its lips a great moan issued, a great roar of escaping breath and despair, leaving behind the body of a beast, the shell of a god. The holy men were called. This was disaster enough: their god was dead, their world would never be the same. And no one could bear to look at the god-killer. Fire crawled away, easily defeated, not by them but by remorse. He could not defend himself against them or himself.

The holy men were ready with a curse, knowing when and how to curse. Fire was open to it, vulnerable for the first time; he felt the curse overwhelm him, because he was guilty. The curse stuck; the people had seen their god killed and they had no will except to give their fear to the holy men, to let them form their collective unspoken curse, to make Fire responsible. And he was.

The fits came on him suddenly; the fits were the curse. The holy men said he was possessed by an avenging spirit, the spirit of the dead god-beast. For this contingency, they had a plan. Things were comfortably familiar again; the old ones read the laws and the young ones carried out the laws. Weakened by fits, clearly possessed, too ill to defend himself but strong enough to travel, he was now the "one-invaded-by demons," and had to be cast out.

But they could not send him away until the proper rituals had been performed. So, naked before them, further sickened by their greedy hate, his eyes rolling and seeing things no one else could see, his fear unmanned him, made him tremble and wince, shudder and cower like a fawn, as they tormented and neutralized him. He wept and shouted and was restrained. After the rituals had been accomplished, they cast him out into the forest alone, well beyond the safe circle of their camp, and according to the law they would hunt him as they would hunt a wild beast, for three days and three nights. And if they found him, they would kill and eat him—each bone and bit of him, to leave no trace of his shame and to take into themselves his demon's power. Until this happened, or until he was gone for good, there would always be panic lurking just beyond the familiar.

They placed him there away from them as the sun set and they returned; the hunt would begin with the next sunrise. Exhausted, possessed, he fell into unconsciousness gratefully. Everyone was clear now. After the hunt and the ritual of eating him, they would kill a stag in his honor. And for his reinstatement, his return in spirit, they would bury it whole and let it rot, giving food back to the earth. The funeral feast would end it all and new gods would appear and be recognized. The holy men were already convened, between rituals, to select their new god.

WHEN HE AWAKENED, before morning, he was still paralyzed by fear; it gripped him there in the darkness and he ran from it, toward any light that he could see. He had killed the god. He ran toward the dim stars and the moon, terrified and exhausted and growing colder and colder from fear and the raw night surrounding his nakedness. He ran to find hope and he ran to escape from the horror inside himself, from the terror in the forest. He ran without looking where he was going; he ran with his eyes rolling tearless, fixed on the stars and then on the moon, the biggest light in the sky, compelling him. And the earth was dark and silent and all the trees and all the crags were the shape of nameless evil, the forms of terror that he vainly tried to thrust from himself, that made the world so strange to his mind. He had killed the god. He ran impaled by moonlight, tearing at his skin and face, trying to pull himself apart, ripping at the forest around him, clutching at crumbling rocks, climbing and biting the hillsides, swallowing and gagging on mouthfuls of earth. And then he went up and over a cliff, falling into a deep, moving river in the darkness.

He had not seen the bank nor had he seen the dark rush of the river beside it. Once in the river, he swam by instinct, trying in spite of himself to stay alive. Thrashing around in the swirl of water and unable to swim to either bank, he gave up and went limp. His madness relaxing, he let himself—like a willow torn free—be carried swiftly down and through gorges and rapids, and in a while he was far away, rushing and laughing in the swirl—bobbing like a naked strip of bark, bruised but still conscious, still mad, laughing now at the panorama above and around him: the narrow gorge, the spinning stars, the brief flashes of white water lapping out of the blackness, the formless, insistent, powerful surge of black water that carried him farther and farther away. He laughed and went more limp, giving himself up to the power and the blackness, and in that way he spent the rest of the night.

The surge calmed as a gorge widened into a valley—a wide alluvial plain preceding the sea. He felt released from all powers, the river's and the demon's, and was gradually coming back to himself, into that good morning, when a hulk loomed in front of him. Then it was swerving toward him. He fought down his panic and reached up to attack as it rose over him, darkening the gray sky. He found a handhold and felt the familiar form of a tree, a great floating tree which carried him along, threatening to ride over him, to drown him, but he pulled himself up and onto it from the handholds the branches offered. It was large enough to carry several men and had been in the water long enough to ride evenly, without spinning. But it moved in wide arcs and the motion of it made him dizzy; he hung on and closed his eyes—resting there, twirling down the river, now a much slower and wider river.

Back upriver at the camp, they went out at sunrise to hunt him; they quickly tracked him all the way to the river but he was nowhere in sight. The next three days they hunted up and down their side of the river, searching for signs, but there were none. The elders were dismayed. He had disappeared and might return in any form; had the god's avenging spirit possessed him or had he possessed it? For months they lived in fear, waiting for him to return in the form of a living demon and for his retribution to be visited upon them. But he did not return. They waited to see if new gods would come to protect them from the anger of the old dead god.

And one night a panther attacked the flock and killed several reindeer; the men came in force to kill it, but it was already dead—impaled on the horns of a great stag—in death, at least, a strange, beautiful stag. No one ever remembered seeing it before and many immediately believed that it gave a special meaning to this curious, unlikely event. The panther was killed by a dying stag—and that was enough, holiness enough for them. And they came to worship stags and forget about their old god—and about Fire. They said he had become the panther impaled by the stag, and that was all there was to it.

But the truth was more difficult. For he had ridden out the river, had ridden the back of the tree, and, as the next day passed, he found that he was himself again and that he was tired and hungry and cold, naked and alone and yet eager to get on with finding food, finding his way to some new way of life. He was better prepared than most to survive; when he faced a beast he was facing only a beast, not a demon. Even the dim memories of his night of terror faded without explanation; he associated them with his possession, his little death, his night of the moon.

There was no time to think about the past, because the present was filled with real dangers and his survival was uncertain. But the past thought of him, perhaps, because on the shore he sometimes thought he saw something or someone waiting for him, stalking him. He waited until the floating tree bore in on an eddy, a fortunate current toward the shore, and he dove in and swam toward the shore, using the last bit of his strength to reach it. The land was swampy there and in the shallows were snakes and alligators—big enough to give him trouble—so he climbed into a tree cleft. He needed to sleep to regain enough strength to find food.

It was afternoon when he awoke and he knew he had to work quickly. He found a forked stick and used it to catch two snakes, which he ate raw. Snakes were rare and a delicacy where he had lived; it was a good omen. He slept again in the tree that night and by morning was feeling strong. He knew it was not safe to stay for long in one place without fire; the beasts would find him eventually and he was defenseless, until he had fire and fire-hardened sticks as spears. The river was too wide and swift for the beasts—including the alligators, who stayed in the swamps and on the banks of the river away from the dangerous currents. He killed and ate again: snakes, frogs, a salamander.

The river would be the safest place. He climbed out on a limb above the bank and waited until a sizable floating tree seemed likely to swirl in close to shore. The river was filled with much debris and in no time one snag came in close enough for him to swim out to it and ride it down-river, looking for a less swampy and dangerous area. He rode the log for a day and a night, and he felt safe there —even in the cold darkness. By morning the landscape had changed; the river was narrow again and running between firm banks covered with pines; beyond there were hills and beyond them mountains—tall ones but not so tall as the white-tipped ones familiar to him on the path from summer to winter.

The water was quickening here. He got off the snag and swam to shore with some difficulty. In a few more miles the river would funnel through another gorge; he could tell that from the white rush of water around the shoreline boulders. The land on this shore was more to his liking. Soon he found flint and had a small fire going. He gathered a pile of wood, enough for several days, and by nightfall had built a shelter of wood and branches leaning against a sheer wall—there were outcroppings of rock all through the rolling hills dotted with clumps of pines and wild oak. He waited by the fire that night—his hunger was growing enormous again—and pulled out and braided strands of his hair into a noose for a trap. Before it was light he set two traps in rabbit runways, and by noon,.the warm sun found him gorging on two rabbits and roasting acorns in his fire. He rested and made coverings for his feet from the skins and gathered wood again for his fire, which would keep the beasts that gathered at night from attacking. The next day he ate rabbit again, and he made fishhooks from the bones and wound grass into a tight vine-cord. The entrails of the rabbit were good bait, and he caught two fish before the line broke. He ate again and banked his fire; beside it he weaved more lines which he kept with him at all times.

It was a good place he had found—fish and small game and even large game. He hunted for flints and for a stout pole. He fractured the flints he found—one into a hand ax and the other into likely tips for arrows and spears. He made arrows and three spears—wedging the flints into the poles and binding them with hair and grass vines. He stalked a herd of deer, hunting most of the day, and killed one of them. He treated the skin with a mixture of bark and water, rubbing it down; and the meat, more than he could eat, he cut in strips and dried in the sun. The dead game drew a panther and wolves, but they would not come into his fire; he kept a supply of stones to drive them off. They were not starving in such a game-laden country, so he was sure they would not attack. From the deer bones he made tools—adzes and fishhooks and a spear—and from the antler bones he made a fine bone knife.

Soon he had a good camp and he could have stayed there the rest of his life were it not for his loneliness for his own kind. And were it not for the forms he sometimes saw or sensed beyond the light of his fire—shapes of dead gods, the apparitions of his guilt and exile. He roamed the area, sometimes staying as much as two days away from his camp, but nowhere on these trips did he see signs of human life. He had never been separated from people for any length of time, except for the week of purification prior to his initiation into manhood. Then, as now, he found himself listening for human sounds, hearing none; looking up, hoping a shadow belonged to a human form. Disappointed at first, gradually he became frightened, the same fear that had overwhelmed him when he was cast from the village. Without them, he did not belong to anything or anyplace or anyone; without them everything, everyplace—himself—was without a name, without a meaning.

Superior to them, he needed them to feel his singularities; a part of them, he needed them to feel he was alive.

He hunted for his future needs and dried the deer meat quickly in the hot sun. He gathered several hand axes from his supply and began cutting pine trees, chopping them into lengths, to build his own version of a floating tree. He built his raft by the bank and tied the logs together, winding them around and around with vines and woven grass. When the raft was finished, he stored his jerked meat in a waterproof bag of skins, tied everything down—including tools and extra skins—and pushed off into the main current of the river, keeping the raft off the bank with a long pole. The river soon entered a gorge strewn with boulders. The raft rode high and bobbed and twirled down through the rapids, until he was weak from dizziness and from the fatigue of pushing off from the boulders and trying to keep the raft from beaching or breaking up.

The first day he stopped at the end of the rapids, well after it was dark, and slept there wedged by boulders until morning. After the gorge, the river widened and split up into meandering tributaries, some so small that he could barely get his raft through. Then the river would come back together again and swell along day after day. The river passed through country heavily timbered by trees that he had never seen—the bark was red and rough like a winter stag and the branches were feathery and almost blue. He stopped one night and built a fire of this red bark, but it did not burn well. The forest was dank with ferns and moss. The air was warmer. The next morning he saw a huge expanse of water not far ahead. He rode the raft all the way to the shallows where the river broached the sand dunes and spilled into the sea; he had never seen the sea before, but sensed it was too large to travel across and too strange to test.

Beached there he waited, resting, taking all the newness in. And before a shadow fell or a sound signaled, people stole up around him—an inner circle of men and beyond, at a safe distance, women and children. They took him to their camp high on the cliffs above the sea. Short, squat, energetic-looking, they were all naked, even the men; and the tips of their spears were made of wood. Their camp was

crude and filthy; he saw human and animal waste everywhere. Living with them would be better than existing
alone, but not much.

When they saw him, skin-draped and tall, his blond
hair flowing and his blue eyes shining with strangeness,
intelligence, and contempt, they thought he was the river
god. They believed the river was a god and that it took
on many forms—beasts, storms, floods, men, and death. The
river was called "the-sea-that-moves-on," and it was easier
for them to comprehend than the sea. They were terrified
of the sea, dreaded anything associated with it, created
endless, hopeless propitiations. If he had been found in
the sea or come from the sea, they would have killed him.
Instead, they made him welcome. The river had served
him well to the end. They devoured the rest of his jerky
and marveled at his skins and tools.

He caused a celebration that lasted for days; he was
given young women for his pleasure and was feasted until
he could not stand: fish of many kinds, including shellfish,
and tough sea-birds. These people did not hunt nor herd;
they lived on fish, which they gathered in hand-woven nets
of simple design; they used primitive spears in the surf and
in the river. When the sea fell back, they scooped up
clams and scallops, abalones and cockles. Inland there were
wild fruits and berries. The sea kept them busy, but they
were never in need; they had created an easygoing culture
deriving from the things of the sea and the river and from
the great terrifying storms that roared in from the sea.

He lived there with them and soon learned their simple
language. He took for himself two of their better women
—taller and not as heavy as the others and with good
teeth (a rarity) and pleasant manners. They reminded him
of the women of his own people. He sometimes thought of
his wife and children, but they were as dead to him as he
was to them. The people built him a fine shelter, according
to his directions, of woven branches and vines covered with
river mud. It was set apart, with a view of both the river
and the sea. And they would not let him gather food or
fish or do anything for himself—and they had so many
special feasts in his honor that he grew fat and lazy.

Gradually, he realized that they thought he was a god,

and he tried to tell them that he was not, that he came from the origin of their river and that he had been lost. But everything he told them seemed to make them believe more strongly that he was a god; his explanations became part of the tribe's mythology; his exploits coming down to them were told and retold in countless distorted variations over the evening fires. Both his women bore him children; and with each birth, mother and child were treated with deference, special regard—because they had mingled with and had come from him. He was both free and honored, but he was still lonely. These people, even more than his own people, were like children and not true companions. He despised himself as an "idler-after-women."

He lazed about, growing tired of his inactivity and of the stupidity of the people he had found. But he did not move on, for they knew of no other people and they traveled many miles up and down the coast between this and another great river. Also he had had journey enough to last a lifetime. Several times he went hunting and tried to show the others how to use flint-tipped spears and bow and arrow, but they were not hunters and it was not in them to be so. When a bear appeared, they turned and ran, while he used his spear to stop it before it killed him. His daring confirmed his godhead, but he would not hunt such large game again with fools. So, he walked alone far from camp, stalking game but rarely killing. Sometimes on a distant ridge or outlined against a sunset, he thought he saw the familiar figure stalking him, the god of his exile, or its spirit, free in the wild places.

He watched the women go to the sea and gather the shellfish, and it was there that he discovered the movement of the tides. They had always gone in the morning and sometimes the sea-god rolled back the sea for them and sometimes it did not. But he watched and saw that the lowest point was reached a little later each day. Excitedly, he tried to explain this to the elders, but they did not understand, insisting that the tides were at the whim of the sea-god. So, for many days he noted the height of the sun when the tide was lowest, and the day came when he was sure. He pointed to the sea, telling the elders to send the women then because the tide was out and would stay out long enough for them to gather shellfish. The elders obeyed him and were not surprised to find that he had been right. From then on he was asked when the women should go to gather shellfish, and each time he knew. To the people it seemed that he controlled the sea and was in fact the highest of all gods: the "one-who-comes-from-the-river-and-rules-the-sea."

He was fascinated by his discovery and spent day after day, night after night, close by the sea watching the tides lap at the sticks he poked in the sand to mark its progress. He discovered two highs and two lows in a day and a night. To see the first night low they came to the beach —all the people with torches, to gather the bounty of shell-fish—and there was a great celebration and feasting. They rejoiced in his name. He let them think he was a god, let them think anything they wanted; they were such inferior people that it was not long before he came to think of himself as something of a god.

But this land he had come to was one where the earth shook and rolled and collapsed cliffs and sent the river spilling over its banks like water from a bowl and the sea roaring inland in great waves, like watery hands reaching up for victims. He was a stranger and knew nothing of the quaking earth and the great seas that were sometimes thrown up across the land. They knew, these simple people, but they thought he was a god and that when he told them to gather shellfish that he would certainly hold back the wall of water as he had done before. If he could control the sea over and over again, then why not at any time? And they had never associated the great waters with the quaking earth, because only rarely did the great waves follow closely on the quaking. They thought that the quaking earth was the sea-god beneath them, and that they floated on an island between seas and rivers and that the water was everywhere, except for the land between the two rivers.

So, one day he gave his advice as usual to go at the low tide for shellfish gathering; almost all the women of the village went. At first they thought it was a great boon; the waters pulled back even farther than anyone could ever remember, pulled back suddenly beyond the lowest of the low points, uncovering new beds of clams, giant clams, and abalones studding rocks now bare for the first time. But a great wave followed; the few who saw it coming screamed and began to run but they were too far from shore and an immensity of gray water fell like a collapsing hillside and their screams were soon drowned and in seconds all the women were gone. From the heights the others heard it break against the land, felt the heavy thud of it, and saw that where the women had been working was now only gray heavy water swirling, retreating.

The catastrophe was complete—only a few old or sick women were left in the tribe, and the girl children had died with their mothers and the surviving infants would probably die without them. The tribe too would probably dwindle away now. The uncommon threat of extinction had suddenly gathered down on them and their terror turned to hate and that hate turned on the man-god they had trusted to hold back the sea. They took him and his women—who had stayed behind because they did not have to work like the other women—took them silently, purposefully, to the highest cliffs above the sea. He argued for only a little while and then relaxed, knowing the inevitable had finally come to him. The women screamed and were bound and gagged to keep them quiet. The children were frightened, but they did not understand.

They first threw the children off the cliff onto the water and rocks below, and then the two women, their eyes bugged with terror, swooning. They made him watch until the sea had claimed the bodies or until there were no more signs of life. And then they grabbed him and he too was tossed from the cliff and fell, describing a slow arc, silently frightened, alone, to the sharp rocks and their finality below. He would not escape this time, he knew; even as he crashed, he realized that he had wondered about this moment all his life. He felt the salt water wash his wounds, felt the broken bones of his body grate and twist, felt himself dying. He took a long time to die; he kept on dying, and dying still more. He was in awe that he should experience such a thing, this ending, this final flowing away of everything, this washing away of himself, out of himself, into the sea. He knew that it was important that he was dying, important to himself, but important beyond that.

He had been alive and now he was dying, and it was important that he knew this last knowing too. He kept wondering about it, could not get enough of these last moments of his life. The god-beast of his exile seemed to be with him, to join him there on the improbable rocks; it seemed to speak to him, to tell him stories, intricate, ghastly stories about his life and all life, about his death and all death; they laughed together, they wept too, and finally they embraced.

A Simple Experiment

Muriel Rukeyser

WHEN a magnet is
struck by a hammer
the magnetism spills out of
the iron.

The molecules
are jarred,
they are a mob going
in all directions

The magnet is
shockéd back
it is no magnet but
simple iron.

There is no more
of its former
kind of accord
or force.

But if you take
another magnet
and stroke the iron
with this,

it can be
remagnetized
if you stroke it
and stroke it,

stroke it
stroke it,
the molecules

can be given
their tending grace

by a strong magnet
stroking stroking
always in the same direction,
of course.

Answering Questions

Michael Goldman

Wʜʏ am I lying there? What is time?
You answer hard questions. I bring you home.
The question you are is why am I here?
What does it cost not to be there?

Not to be you? I gladly accept.
The question you are is why not someone else?
The question you answer is never what if?
Anyone else would be larger than life.

Anyone else and I bring her home
and ask her hard questions like what is the time?
And she answers me asking me what does it cost
to have known what you missed, to have known what you
    missed?

And the question is what have I done with your life?
And the answer is answer me, answer for life.

Safari

Alfred Chester

Our appointment was for after lunch, down the street from my house in a little formal park full of trees and flowers called the Garden of the Frog. I say it's called the Garden of the Frog, though I have heard only one person, a cab driver, refer to it as such, and that was two years ago when I first moved into the neighborhood. All the local people call it the Cattle Market Garden since long ago there was a cattle market somewhere around, perhaps right on that spot. When I visualize the park I imagine that in front of it is a statue as large as a squatting man, but much broader, a sparkling granite frog on a low red brick pedestal. But it isn't really there. In any case, whatever the place is named, for a fact on wet autumn nights its paths and the surrounding streets are filled with frogs. You don't hear them, as you do around ponds in the spring, because they're silent. But if you go by in the dark, you can see their eyes gleaming and the outline of their lumpy bodies in the mud. Or occasionally you see one leap through the rain, from nowhere to nowhere, flung up by the evil spirits that frogs are supposed to contain. By morning they've disappeared.

I came early, not having eaten, and sat in the garden waiting for Gerald. It was terribly hot and I was feeling sick in my stomach and my brain. The park was empty except for myself and a man about my age or somewhat younger, a laborer in blue jeans and a blue denim jacket who always seems to appear in the garden when I'm there. He never sits on my bench, or even close to me, but always on another bench and at some distance, and he watches me slyly until I become so uncomfortable I have to get up and leave. Sometimes I try to stare boldly back at him, flinging my eyes up suddenly like six-shooters; in which case, he nods and smiles in a friendly, neighborly way and begins observing my feet or my hands, as if they might clue him in on something.

The afternoon I was waiting for Gerald, this laborer (if he is a laborer, he has a lot of time for idling), or this man disguised as a laborer, was sitting in the sun near the giant irises. I was in the shade of a tall umbrella pine not far from where the statue of the frog would be if it existed.

Finally Gerald appeared in chinos and a plaid flannel shirt. At ten yards or more away, you would think he was fifteen years old, though in fact he's almost at the other end of middle age. He is small and thin like a boy, but not muscular, full of quick nervous energy, and his hair is still very blond. If there is any gray in his hair, it doesn't show.

"Shall we go?" I said, standing up.

"Where?" He seemed startled.

"Oh. I thought . . . don't we have a date to go hunting scorpions?" It occurred to me then that though I'd known we were going to the country, for some reason I was wearing a jacket and a tie and my narrow Italian shoes, bought three years ago at Macy's, and hardly ever worn. I felt ridiculous and wondered if I shouldn't go home and change.

"Of course we do. But where shall we go?"

"How would I know? I've never gone scorpion-hunting before. You're supposed to be taking me, aren't you? What's that you have there?"

He was holding a large can of powdered milk, or rather a large powdered milk can, because when he took the lid off there was nothing inside but a pair of cuticle scissors and some whitish dust.

"Is that the equipment?" I asked, remembering that he'd mentioned on the phone about bringing along the equipment.

He didn't answer, or if he did, I don't remember what he said. It was certainly not an informative answer. Possibly he drummed with his fingers on the side of the can or smiled broadly but blankly to show me his ugly wizard teeth or simply fixed his hollow, pale, pale blue eyes on me.

(I might as well add here that one of my shortcomings is to not necessarily wait for an answer.)

I said, "Well, where do we go?"

He was silent and looked puzzled, as if he were expecting me to decide. I suppose he does things like that to be irritating—imagine, at *his* age!—and though I know it's what he wants, I nonetheless get irritated.

Somehow, finally, we started off.

We followed the main road out of town, out to where it descends with sudden steepness into a eucalyptus and palm suburbia that I find as painful to walk through as the street I was born on. Most of the houses were built by Europeans during the days just before independence, and now most of the Europeans have gone, so the houses sit like crumbling futuristic fantasies, shuttered, chained, empty, eviscerated. Walking past, you get the feeling that people must be secretly slipping off to other planets, and that soon you will be left alone here, that you'll have the solitary run of the world along with all its antique futuristic houses.

About halfway through this suburbia, we left the main road and continued downhill via footpaths to the floor of the little Drin valley, a practically uninhabited—there are one or two shacks around—pasture land through which a little river runs. The day Gerald and I went into the valley, the river was dry and the land had a dead, burned look; that was before the rain, of course. I once saw a goat born in this valley, on a soft afternoon in early spring when the grass was high and the river full. A boy about eight years old was out pasturing the mother goat when suddenly the kid arrived. It happened very quickly, almost as if she'd stopped to pee, and then the little boy took the kid up in his arms and started off home, or wherever, while the mother goat ran after him bleating, and with a great globe of blood hanging out behind like crimson udders and swinging as she ran.

I was remembering this, when Gerald said: "I had a letter from Rudolph Kitkin the other day." I would like to write here "and my heart almost sprang out of my mouth"—but it didn't; it sank with a slow, heavy bitterness.

"Did you?" I tried to sound casual. I know Gerald can

read my mind. It's happened too often to be coincidence.

"He's in Florida visiting his parents."

"Oh?" It was hotter in the valley than it had been in the town and I felt sick right down through my body, even to my feet, which were growing thicker in their tight Italian shoes. To clear the air, I said, "Did you know Rudolph once had a pet goat?"

"Yes, indeed. I saw it dead, in fact, on his kitchen table. And Rudolph sitting over it, like a Soutine *Yeshiva bucher*. He'd injected stimulants into it, hoping to revive it. He said, 'If you don't object to the centerpiece, sit down.' I did object, naturally. 'Think,' I told him, 'you don't know what it died of. It could be some virus.' But it was a cute little animal when it was healthy, didn't you think so?"

"I never saw it."

"No!" he exclaimed, pretending surprise. He knew perfectly well the goat had died before I'd ever come to Africa. "How's that?"

In spite of myself, I explained how it was I'd never seen the goat, and in doing so—such am I—forgot he was putting me on. "He used to tell me about it a lot, though. He could imitate its lovely little bleating sound—and the sound of its hoofs coming down the marble stairs of the house. Clip-clop. Clip-clop. Rudolph made it sound very dainty and delicate, the hoofs on the marble stairs. The goat thought Rudolph was its mother and always slept with him at night."

"That doesn't surprise me a bit," Gerald said. "I mean, naturally all babies think whoever cares for them is their mother."

As we walked, he pointed out shrubbery, grasses, and even small flowers. To me the land had looked parched, but since Gerald is extremely observant, the valley came to life. Not to much of a life, but a life just the same. Gerald remembers what he looks at, classifies what he sees, will recollect a plant if he comes across it again. He remembers smells and colors and shapes. The world I live in has few details and practically no names, and seldom repeats itself. I see a large anonymous blur that is every day replaced by another large anonymous blur.

It was a hard walk across the valley, and we went clear

across. You would think the land here had been battered into shape by earthquakes, tidal waves, and stupendous molten comets. It rises, sinks, breaks open, mushrooms up in small plateaus, rolls like corrugated steel for stretches of fifty yards or more. The animals, when they graze, have many wrinkles to nibble in. But it is hard land to walk over, especially at Gerald's rapid pace, for though he's much older than I am, he's as sure-footed as a goat and as energetic. I'm flabby and easily winded.

As we came down one rise of land, there appeared an immense cement structure which I'd never seen before, like the foundation of an unbuilt or perhaps destroyed house. It had chicken wire nailed down all over it, and a young man was busy at the wire. Either he was removing some or adding some. Or he might have been nailing it down more firmly. For some reason we had to walk right over this structure, and then a little further on we reached a narrow tarred road that had bamboo and rushes growing on either side. I knew this road. If we turned south on it, as in a moment we did, it would lead us back to the main road and not more than a quarter of a mile beyond where we'd turned off it, in suburbia. In other words, we had crossed the valley for nothing.

I contained myself, however, until we reached the main road; then I asked: "How much further do we go?"

"About a mile or a mile and a half. Just beyond the cemetery."

"Will you please tell me why we went clear across that valley when we could have gone along the road and saved ourselves three miles at least?"

"We couldn't have. The main road doesn't come down this way."

"It does so. We're on it now."

"This isn't the same road we left," he said calmly.

"It is so."

"It is not."

I felt too sick to go on protesting. Besides we were now at the foot of the mountain and passing under a dome of eucalyptus, so a soothing draft came over me. Here the road breaks into two, one part going straight up the mountain, the other part winding around the base before rising up to meet and join the first part, becoming one again and unrolling among forests and cliffs and at last along the beaches of the cape. We walked the lower road, past the Catholic Cemetery and then past the Animal Rest Home, a cemetery for dogs and cats.

"I've seen only two scorpions in my life," I said. "Present company excepted. One in Greece. I think I killed it. And one in Arizona during the war, on the wall of my brother's outhouse."

"Really? That's strange." He spoke as though he didn't believe I had ever seen a scorpion, and I wondered if I weren't making the story up. As I thought about my scorpions, they grew vaguer and more fictitious. They became no more real, nor mine, than those I'd heard about in Mexico, where they are said to drop from the trees by the handful.

Presently, as lightly and casually as I could, I said: "I think I'm being poisoned."

Gerald cupped his hand around his ear. He often likes to pretend he is hard of hearing. "Who?" he said.

"What who? *Me!*"

"Who are you poisoning?" he asked, looking me full in the face and giving me a flash of all his wicked yellow teeth.

"I'm not poisoning anyone. I think someone is poisoning me."

"Why, do you feel sick?"

"I feel strange."

"Don't you always feel strange? You always complain about feeling strange."

"I feel stranger than usual."

"But *how?*"

Of course I didn't want to tell him, for I suspected him of being, if not precisely my poisoner, then certainly involved in my poisoning, in charge of it, as it were, and probably for no better motive than to hear me speak of my reactions. With a big smile, I said: "Are you poisoning me, by any chance?"

"Me? You're joking, surely."

"Am I?"

"Why on earth would I want to poison you?"

"Why not? Just for fun, I suppose. What else is there to do around here?"

He nodded. "Not much, that's true."

After some silence and a little guilty grief, I said: "I hope it doesn't offend you, my asking."

He patted me on the back. "Oh, no, not at all."

Dear Reader, imagine a state of loneliness and isolation so profound that you have to apologize to your poisoner. Yet, is it a real poison that Gerald, assuming it *is* Gerald— and who else could it be?—feeds me? It needn't be.

Sometimes I think Gerald is God, at least a local god, or more exactly, a local demon. Africa is not the same as other continents, despite its revolutions, and Gerald has lived here so long that magic and sorcery are more part of his nature than science or the ten commandments. I do actually hear drums at his approach; I can see the bone and the ring through his nose; I can see the hideous paint on his face. He is a witch doctor using the body of a mild English missionary. I believe his mind can create things, can make them up as he goes along, *real* things (so to speak), like this road we were on, or the valley we'd just crossed over, or the mountain above us. If the world is illusion, why shouldn't Gerald be the cause of some of those illusions? I know this sounds insane. I probably am insane. Still and all, can't a madman be logical and right?

If I see too much of Gerald, he spreads insidiously through my life like ink on blotting paper. I go out at night and hear a strange bird cry in the trees, and I think: that's Gerald. Or a dog baying. If I'm with someone else—but it is rare that I am—I might easily say, "Listen! Do you hear that bird? It's Gerald. He can turn himself into a bird." And to protect myself from what I believe to be true and also from appearing too crazy, I wax poetical-comical. "A demon bird. He turns himself into a demon bird."

"What's a demon bird?" I have been asked.

"A black parrot-like animal with tremendous wings who cannot be seen but only heard at night. During the day it turns blue and flies continually, so you can't see it against the sky. At sunset, its color deepens and becomes flecked with red. It darkens to violet—and then finally black again.

If it flies at night, which it hardly ever does, since it prefers to sit nearby in a tree screaming or hooting, some of its feathers sparkle like stars."

"Does it eat?"

"It eats you and me. Our dreams. Our secret thoughts."

Or possibly the crying birds and the baying dogs are in Gerald's pay. They are bribed by him to sound off at the most appropriate moments, when most likely to horrify me.

One summer afternoon I went bathing at the vast empty beach on the cape. After a while I started feeling strange, maybe a little sunstruck—giddy and nauseated, but yet exultant. Trying to calm myself, I paced around in the sand; Gerald was much in my mind, like a huge dirty joke. Then suddenly I was looking at the towering sand cliffs to the east, and I felt sure—without fright, mind you, with laughter, rather—that Gerald's smiling head would appear above those hills like a gigantic puppeteer over his stage, like a dripping leviathan surfacing out of a swimming pool.

And, yes, who *are* those inexplicable creatures doing inexplicable things in *my* life?

Who, for example, is the laborer in blue jeans and blue denim jacket? Who are the others I haven't told you about? The scrawny old widow in black who sits on the steps of the cathedral until I pass her on my way down to the market, whereupon she rises and scuttles off the other way; who is she? Who is the stocky middle-aged man who parks his old blue Dauphine opposite the Garden of the Frog every single evening after dark and then walks in what appears to be distracted solitude up and down the path where the musk lily blooms, hiding a stolen broken branch of it behind his back? Is he just out for a stroll? *Is anyone ever just out for a stroll?* Is there any innocence left—the harmless stealing of a flower, walking through a park at night, the cry of a bird that is really a bird, the bay of a dog that smells death or feels hunger, fright, or loneliness, a strange sensation in the body that is not poison or malevolent magic?

A BOY WITH a bulbous head and lots of curly brown hair on top of it came down the road hailing us dourly. His clothes were torn and he was shoeless, and the nail of the big toe on his right foot had been torn or eaten away. The quick was festering. Actually, it looked as though it were fermenting.

Gerald and the boy shook hands.

"Have you come for more scorpions?" the boy asked.

"Yes." To me, Gerald said: "The last time I was here this boy helped me."

The three of us continued along the road for a few yards, and when Gerald was about to lead us up a rise, the boy said: "No, it's not any good up there."

"Why not? It was very good last time."

"Yes, but it isn't any good now. Times change. We should go down there now." He pointed off the road to a kind of peninsula or small cliff that was really the bank of a river gone dry.

"Do you think we ought to listen to him?" Gerald asked me.

"How would I know?"

"That's true."

"There are more scorpions there than up ahead," said the boy.

Gerald raised his arms as if in surrender, and we followed the boy down off the road and onto the peninsula.

It was greener here than in the valley, but just as hot, since there weren't any trees, only herbal shrubs and a great many palmetto bushes. I took off my jacket and threw it onto a bush, then stood feeling dizzy.

Almost immediately, Gerald spied a scorpion hole. (The word "spied" is a little quaint, but it suits Gerald.) As far as I was concerned, it could have been an anthole, except it was slightly larger and more oval in shape. Gerald tore a palmetto fan out of its bush and, squatting, stuck the long stem end down the scorpion hole. He jiggled it a while.

"The point is—" he began, then interrupted himself with a cry: "There! He's grabbed it!"

I wondered if he were really excited. You can never tell with him if he really cares about anything. I don't believe he does. I think the only thing he genuinely cares about is watching things squirm. Things and people.

"Look," he said.

He let go of the leaf and I could see it give tiny but definite jerks, as if it were being tugged at inside the hole.

"The trick is to get the leaf up with the scorpion still holding on the other end of it." Slowly, he slid the stem up, but when the end came into sight, there was no scorpion. "Damn," said Gerald, sticking the leaf down the hole again.

Meanwhile the boy was standing alongside me, looking dazed while he chewed on the stem of a palmetto leaf.

"The saliva is supposed to hypnotize the scorpion," Gerald explained, looking up at us. He didn't explain, nor did I ask, why he used his leaf dry.

The boy examined his chewed stem, and evidently deciding it was hypnotic enough began walking around, eyes down, looking for a scorpion hole. I suddenly realized that the land was filled with them—not porous, exactly, but there was every foot or two one of those oval openings. This didn't frighten me, but since I felt it should, that if it didn't it was because I was bewitched or poisoned, I said to Gerald: "Isn't it dangerous with all these scorpions lurking under us?"

"Probably," he smiled, jiggling.

I followed the boy to the edge of the peninsula. He now had acquired the torn plastic sole of a Japanese sandal, and he was shoving his palmetto stem down a hole. He squatted over the hole with the intense look of a fisherman waiting for a tremble on the line. He seemed to listen intently.

"Got it!" he cried, and flung his arm back. The scorpion, having come up with its claws on the end of the stem, came loose of it as the boy's arm went back. It sailed through the air and landed almost at my feet. It didn't look at all like the other scorpions I've seen, or that I imagine I've seen. This one had a brownish amber shell like a beetle but oilier and more translucent. The body itself was quite dark and shiny, like tortoiseshell, the big front pincers somewhat lighter; the six side legs and the segmented tail with the stinger at the end of it were palest of all, almost yellow. Also it was less than three inches long from front claws to stinger. The scorpions I remember from the past had tan chalky bodies and were five or six inches long at least, perhaps longer.

It stood without moving, its tail curled over its back; it was waiting, sensing a trap, but nonetheless dignified. The boy threw the plastic sole down on the scorpion, catching the front half under but leaving the tail exposed and wagging.

"The scissor!" the boy called to Gerald, who was still squatting over his hole.

"What, have you caught one?" Gerald said, and came running with the milk can.

The boy grabbed the scissor out of his hand and quickly snipped off a couple of segments of tail.

"You've cut too much off," said Gerald, annoyed.

"No, it's better this way."

Gerald waved his arms helplessly. "All you really need to cut off is the stinger and the poison sack just behind. Then it's perfectly harmless. You've ruined the look of it now."

"It's better this way," the boy repeated, unmoved, then picked the scorpion up and dropped it into the milk can. With the scissor he punched a couple of air holes in the lid.

"What do you do with it now that you've caught it?" I asked.

"Nothing," said Gerald. "You can look at it. Or torment it. Or ignore it."

Irritated, I turned to the boy: "Won't it die in there? Can it live without its stinger?"

The boy shoved out his lower lip and, with effort, to be polite, pretended to be interested in the scorpion's destiny. "Yes, it can live all right," he said.

"Can you feed it? What does it eat?"

"Oh, anything." He seemed suddenly inspired. "It especially likes bread crumbs."

Gerald burst into laughter. I felt sorry for myself, and the sun was still very hot. I went and sat on a large rock and looked down at the dry stones of the river bed and thought about being poisoned.

Gerald and the boy continued unearthing scorpions.

Chester / Safari 187

Whenever one was caught, I jumped up and ran to look, so as not to reveal how truly far away I was from the world of the living. Gerald clipped the tails now, cutting off hardly anything. All in all, the boy caught five scorpions and Gerald only one. Such is the sweetness of my soul that I wasn't even glad to see him so defeated. Neither did he himself seem to mind.

When the hunt was over, Gerald offered me a cigarette. I took one puff and a pain went through my body.

"I can't smoke these days," I said, stubbing the cigarette out on the side of the rock. I meant that cigarettes were one of the means by which I was being poisoned.

"You're lucky," said Gerald, picking up my butt and putting it into his pocket. He smoked for a while, standing alongside me. Then he said: "If you surround a scorpion with a ring of fire, he'll investigate all around, and when he finds he can't escape, he'll sting himself in the back of the head. Commit suicide. Isn't that sad?"

Since of course he was really talking about me, I made a noncommittal answer.

He said: "Someone was saying just the other day how well you look lately."

"Who?"

"I can't remember who. Petrelli maybe."

"Who's Petrelli?"

"Surely you know Sanford Petrelli, the historian?"

"Yes, I met him once or twice. But I haven't seen him in eleven years."

"Well, maybe he's seen you," he said significantly. "He's in town, you know."

"No, I didn't know. And I don't care. And I certainly don't care how I look. I feel terrible." Imagine, Reader, if you can, a reasonable way of discussing your health with your poisoner.

Gerald gave the boy a hundred francs. The money was accepted in silence and without any apparent joy or sadness.

After that we followed the main road past the cemeteries and kept to it until we reached the Garden of the Frog. I didn't point out the fact that I had been right about the roads; there was no need to, since of course he knew.

When we stopped at the garden, I invited Gerald up to my apartment for tea.

"I can't," he said. "I want to get to the post office before it closes."

"Oh. But I thought I'd like a scorpion if I could have one."

"I'm sorry, I didn't think. Naturally you can have as many as you like."

We crossed the park and went down the street to my house. Upstairs I found a small cardboard box and Gerald shook three of the scorpions out of the milk can and into my box. After he'd gone, I punched some airholes in the lid and threw a few bread crumbs in among the scorpions.

That was weeks ago, before the rain. Two of the scorpions soon died, and within a few days of each other, one with its pincers close together in front of its face, as if warding off a blow, the other with, as it were, its arms spread wide. The third, however, grew bigger and bolder and stronger-looking as a result of the bread crumbs, or more probably—as I believe, but have no definite evidence of—from sucking out the innards of his brethren through their wounded tails. I noticed that the corpses became progressively more hollow. In any case, the third scorpion, after groveling in its corner for nearly a month, became when I opened the box as frisky as a prizefighter. Whenever I took the lid off, he came rearing from his corner with a little too much speed and energy. His pincers waved, and his tail went over his back menacingly; I think he was even growing another stinger back.

So one dry day last week, not feeling so sickly, I went out to where we'd hunted them and threw everything away, the live scorpion and the dead ones, the bread crumbs and the box. The land has changed a lot since the day we hunted, for the rain came shortly afterward and has fallen, fallen, fallen almost without pause. Though it is already winter, everywhere it is as green as an Irish spring, and under the relentless purplish blackish sky, all is grasses and clovers and bright emerald creepers.

The Landlady's Complaint

Alice Mattison

THESE curly pated boys cooking semen like soup all day
Hoarding semen to dole out if any grateful girl
Curtseys by in a long skirt whispering "a boon, a boon"
These boys could make it in colors, they could sell it
They could preserve flies in hard bright beads of semen
They could pay the rent

what little they know of freedom
the bums, the semen squeezers

I once had a green scarf
Naked but for that feather
I waltzed in long loops
Down River Road: cars piled up
From here to Fulton, horns splattered
Around my ears; chunky jeeps, obese Pontiacs
Angled painfully around me
But I waltzed, those patrolmen pelting me with tickets
Could do nothing, shrugged and went home with all their
    flesh and metal

when I acted lighter than air
I was lighter than air
these boys can't do it

Now I'm the landlady and the land
Plowed and seeded, inhabited and milked
I know about children moving into me
Curling up in my tight space
I know about mouths taking milk from me
My arm supports a beam and my hand strokes the chimney
I'm the beam, I'm the chimney

these tired ones
trespassers
businessmen doing their business

Women are the land and the people

Your Story

Al Levine

You told me how Caligula had looked for you
And Macro, the colonel in chief of the Praetorian guard
Had put a reward on your head of ten thousand
  sesterces
And how you had lost yourself in the Armenian quarter
  on the top floor of an insula
Being afraid to come out except at night
And how the Emperor had expressed a desire to see your
  head
With two Celtic nose-flutes in the nostrils
And a pneumatic machine pumping air through the neck-
  hole
And how the Emperor had pissed on Macro's foot when he
  couldn't find you
And how Macro had smiled and planted
  the dagger in his soul
Which grew into the German war-sword that split Caligula's
  abdomen like a lobster
And how by this time you had left Rome for Dalmatia
And how you went swimming near Split when the
  Ninth Legion was on your trail
And how the fish covered up the hole that you made in the
  Adriatic when you dove to the bottom
And how Pythagoras the Philosopher was waiting for you
  there
And how the tones of a lute in sea water are three octaves
  lower than they are on land
And how old you are now
And how your apartment here in Naples costs you prac-
  tically nothing

Somehow I believe you.

Greeks in Persia

Al Levine

This language, which once was the language of kitchen
   gardens,
Of small white houses shining in the sun like the baby
   teeth of the mountains,
Now is lost in the gray winds of this great plain,
Swirled between the hooves of the king's horses
As the wind carries it away.
The word: bread, The word: sister, the word: sleep
Carried through this unsleeping void,
These are sounds as small as the stars in the night
Or the pebbles that roll with the storm
Or the sands that fling themselves against our cheeks.
How   closely   a   few   olive   trees   could   fill   the   tiny   valleys
         When the spring leaves sang

The Various Isolated:
W. C. Williams' Prose

Gilbert Sorrentino

In many poor and sentimental households it is a custom to have cheap prints in glass frames upon the walls. These are of all sorts and many sizes and may be found in any room from the kitchen to the toilet. The drawing is always of the worst and the colors, not gaudy but almost always of faint indeterminate tints, are infirm. Yet a delicate accuracy exists between these prints and the environment which breeds them. But as if to intensify this relationship words are added. There will be a "senti-ment" as it is called, a rhyme, which the picture illumi-nates. Many of these pertain to love. This is well enough when the bed is new and the young couple spend the long winter nights there in delightful seclusion. But chil-birth follows in its time and a motto still hangs above the bed. It is only then that the full ironical meaning of these prints leaves the paper and the frame and starting through the glass takes undisputed sway over the household.

—Kora in Hell (1920)

WILLIAM CARLOS WILLIAMS' neglected "Stecher tril-ogy"—*White Mule, In the Money,* and *The Build-Up*—is the best fictional treatment of the immigrant "success story" that we have in American letters. Its power, its secret power, one might almost say, lies in its ability to release the absolute meaning of cultural and financial success in the context of a narrative that is neither comic, tragic, nor satiric. This is no small thing, for the detailing of the failures of the American dream has always demanded, so it seems, a kind of educated and knowledgeable *comment* on the part of the American novelist, lest he seem to be taken in, duped by what appears to be contentment or happiness. So at first glance, or with an eye too used to the patterned assaults upon this success story, the Williams trilogy looks simple, trusting, innocent—almost naïve. "The lovely and uncomplicated past," one might say. We may even take it to be an exercise in nostalgia, to our utter confusion.

Of the writers of Williams' generation (and one may also include most of those who came just after it) whose work is purely American, by which I mean that they wrote of Americans in America, Williams is the sole figure whose work speaks to us with ruthless and persistent clarity, and with a vision of American life which becomes more intense as the years pass and we see what we have come to. This quality is partially achieved by his absolute willingness to forgo "sophisticated" effects in order to discover the essential qualities of the most obscure events; in other words, in his willingness to appear "simple." His entire body of work is a record of continual observation, of the revelation of what he calls the "isolate flecks" in which the whole meaning of a life, or of a cultural milieu, may be contained. Somehow, during almost forty years of the most preposterous ignorance of his fiction on the part of the critical establishment, he captured, by dint of perseverance and his own wide-ranging imagination, the meaning of the shapelessness of American life, buried, as it has always been, in the pettiness of our daily routine, and the "famous," hollow triumphs that speckle it.

His sensibility was so acutely against the grain that his work, to this day, is almost unfathomable to many literary people who have been raised in what has been called the "international tradition" in letters. He does not fit, he is a maverick, his compositions bulk uncomfortably in the landscape of the classical moderns and almost seem to refute them. Nothing fooled him for long because he refused to let "ideas" govern his work. He is sprawling, confused, unfinished, and at the same time brilliant, succinct, crafted—and unfailingly, unerringly dark. Not dark with the tragic, but with the endless defeats of life and—nonetheless—its tenacity. Without sentiment about God, politics, love, the working man, nature, the family, marriage, or children, he is yet uncynical. People are born and live in recurrent confusion; the overwhelming majority of their days is wholly without meaning. In America, this happens in a specific way, a way which makes us specifically American. The imagination, only the imagination, Williams says, will free us from the waste and despair that America has hidden under its continual smile. It is the flight, or the heartbreaking attempt at flight, of the imagination that he seeks to pin down and isolate in all his work.

In the Stecher trilogy, Joe, the husband, a craftsman printer whose major interest in life is honest work well done, becomes a rich man, largely through the goading of his wife, Gurlie. Ironically, it is his stubborn artisan's honesty that shapes his success in the corrupted, get-rich-quick business world in which he is forced to move. Thwarted in his desire as a young man in Germany to attend a university, he is disgusted by the admiration that merely earning big money garners in the United States. Joe knows who he is, and stays that way, battling off as best he can Gurlie's constant prodding to be "fancy." Yet at the end of the trilogy, with his older daughter run off with a hopeless, charming painter, his younger daughter married to a young doctor who has married her even though he does not love her, his son dead in a shotgun accident, and his social life in a kind of limbo because of his anti-British stand on the war, Joe builds the mansion that Gurlie has always wanted. What else is there? The excavators run into granite as they begin digging the foundation, and Joe says, at the end of *The Build-Up,* "No matter. Blast! Blast it out! Blow the damned rock to hell and gone. We're going to have a house like nothing in the neighborhood. Like nothing, like nothing in the neighborhood. Expense be damned." Joe, of course, cares nothing about the house, has never cared about it, nor about the expense. The house is the secretion, one might say, of Joe's trapped imagination. Bewildered in his misery, he seeks a place where that misery might go, since there is no place else for it to find relief but in something that he can afford—out of the wealth he does not care for and cannot really understand.

"The imagination will not down," Williams writes, in 1923 in *The Great American Novel.* "If it is not a dance, a song, it becomes an outcry, a protest. If it is not flamboyance it becomes deformity; if it is not art, it becomes crime." Joe Stecher is only one of the characters of the trilogy demeaned and emptied by the tyranny of "reality."

Where does the artist go to find these bastards of the thwarted imagination? He goes down the street, or around the corner. He takes a ride in his car.

The fact that Williams had everything under his eye, that his laboratory was something so uneventful and banal as the American small town, gave rise to the critical dullness that has always thought of him as a primitive, or a *naïf*, or an "experimental" writer, i.e., one not to be taken seriously, as in "Robert Duncan is an experimental poet." Or, more charitably perhaps, but no less foolishly, as an Eastern Sherwood Anderson. But Williams was a great artist whose creative powers neither flagged nor became ancillary to shifting fads. As *Paterson* is the culmination of his poetic genius, so the Stecher trilogy is that genius's most thorough prose expression.

NOVELS ARE CLUTTERED with all kinds of signals, flashing and gesturing so that the author may direct our attention to a particular configuration of character or plot in order that his work, such as it is, may be made simpler for him, and for us. One thinks of the work of John Cheever, Capote, Norman Mailer, and the master of the technique, John O'Hara, whose characters are presented for inspection and understanding in terms of their very luggage or the brand of cigarettes they smoke. Indeed, in an O'Hara story, "Exactly Eight Thousand Dollars Exactly," these signals are manipulated in reverse, so that the character with whom we expect to be in sympathy turns out to be the heavy. I like to think of this as a writer's joke, or perhaps as an indication of O'Hara's awareness of his own progressive decline as an imaginative writer. Such signals assure us that we are here, oh yes, in the world that we understand; what we "understand" are the signals. When the signals are crassly or obviously used, we are given the popular novel, or the Western or mystery; when deeply or subtly placed, it is a good bet that we are in the presence of the well-crafted, talented, and often slick novel; if the signals are all, they become symbols: we think we are learning something, we are seeing "beneath the surface" of things, but we are seeing nothing at all. Symbols func tion secondarily: if a work has no power on a primary, nonsymbolic level, the most assiduously laid-on symbolism will not rescue it from the inert.

Readers are so passive before this assault of the conventional that they often look for these signals: when they are not there, they feel abandoned, they feel that the work is difficult, or gauche—they feel, perhaps, betrayed. At such times the novel is often forced to yield up that which it does not possess. Those novels that have no symbols at all, nor that can be squeezed to release a few, critics have misnamed "naturalistic" or "realistic" novels.

But signals are gimmicks, elements of craftsmanship, or the lack of it. They allow the writer to slip out from under the problems that only confrontation with his materials can solve. Novels are made of words. The difficulty in writing fiction is that the words must be composed so that they reveal the absolute reality of their prey, their subject —and at the same time, they must be in themselves real, i.e., they do not have to stand for a specific meaning. Here, one may think of Wittgenstein's "Man possesses the capacity of constructing language, in which every sense can be expressed, without having an idea how and what each word means." In *A Novelette*, Williams suggests that even conversation in fiction can be so composed as to remove itself from what characters are "saying." He writes, "The solidity of the pure lends itself by pure design. . . . That would be a writing," he goes on to say, "in which the conversation was actual to the extent that it would be pure design." And further on, he says, "To be a conversation, it must have only the effect of itself, not on him to whom it has a special meaning but as a dog or a store window." (It is, incidentally, this conception of conversation that gives to Williams' characters, in the trilogy, the curious flatness of speech that is often mistaken for accurate transcription—which it is not.)

The words must also have, in their composition, a texture and design we call style. The novel must exist outside of the life it deals with; it is not an imitation. The novel is an invention, something that is made; it is not the expression of "self"; it does not mirror reality. If it is any good at all it mirrors the processes of the real, but, being selective, makes a form that allows us to see these processes with clarity. Signals in novels obscure the actual—these signals are disguised as conversation, physiognomy, clothing, accouterments, possessions, social graces—they satisfy the desire that we be told what we already know, they enable the writer to manipulate his book so that it seems as if life really has form and meaning, while it is, of course, the writer who has given it these qualities. It is the novel, of itself, that must have form, and if it be honestly made we find, not the meaning of life, but a revelation of its actuality. We are not told what to think, but are instead directed to an essence, the observation of which leads to the freeing of our own imagination and to our arrival at the only "truth" that fiction possesses. The flash, the instant or cluster of meaning must be extrapolated from "the pageless actual" and presented in its imaginative qualities. The achievement of this makes a novel which is art: the rest is pastime.

The novel we think of when we hear "this is a real novel" is filled with people, weather, places, and conversation that we recognize instantly—from other "real novels." We all know that plump, perspiring woman who chews gum, the failing ad man with the shakes in the bar at three in the afternoon, the lonely girl from the Midwest who lives down the hall and who befriends the super. Will any of these people do what we do not expect them to do, save as "irony" or surprise? Will they move the story naturally? Are they anything more than the characters we know from movies, instantly recognizable? Their very attitudes are as frozen as the faces of actors playing character roles.

Williams points out, in a lecture touching on *The Sheltering Sky,* the finely wrought art by which Bowles allows a woman on a train to be stripped naked by a man whom she despises. Her disrobing, and subsequent seduction, are brought about by a series of the most delicately crafted events. It could have been easier, certainly, had Bowles used the "exotic-night-in-Africa" signal; but he shapes a situation that is not what one might expect from the scene presented. In keeping with the tone of his novel, she must not *simply* be seduced; her seduction must anticipate the despair and madness bearing down on her. A dozen writers, more highly praised than Bowles, would have simply got her out of her clothes by means of one signal or another, but this artist does not lead his imagination, he allows it its head. The invented character can only reveal the actual if he is the creature of the novelist's *invention,* not a signal whom we stupidly think is doing something "believable."

There seems to be no established critical apparatus to deal with this "signal-less" American novel. Not even after all these years. We are lost in a sea of manners, or blinded into thinking that "characters" are characters. Hubert Selby speaks of the value of "true people as opposed to the blatant REAL people" in certain fiction—that latter in which we read dialogue as accurate as a tape recording, i.e., false dialogue. They do, these "REAL people," believable things in terms of the novel's development. Are we all mad? Fifty years after Joyce and Lewis, Williams and Ford, we search for "flesh and blood" characters who "walk off the page." Somehow we wish the novel to be a reflection of the world that the news tells us is true. The "facts" are paramount, the imagination is trapped, thwarted, unrelieved, until it must find its release, finally, in trash, or in Anglo-European fiction that lulls us into thinking that it is addressed to us—who have no traditions, and whose best art has always appeared in staggered and lonely configurations that seem insane or deformed.

Doomed as are so many novels to chic caricature, awash with signals and creaking symbolism, filled with accurate conversation, real people, or the pop-art situations and characters that substitute for the imagination in the swill of black humor, what attention can be paid to novels that eschew these conventions? What happens to that writer whose imagination composes not the pseudo-reality, but those facets of reality that bring what we do not know —or do not wish to know—about ourselves into the light? Charles Olson, in his essay "Billy the Kid," defines "misery" as no more than "a characterization of unrelieved action or words," and goes on to say that the history of the United States has stayed, and stays, unrelieved. "And thus loses what it was before it damn well was history, what urgency or laziness or misery it was to those who said and did what they did." He also says: "All we got is what the best men have kept their eye on. No figures, no forms, no known largenesses whatsoever. Zero." Thirty years earlier, in *The Great American Novel,* Williams was saying:

> America is a mass of pulp, a jelly, a sensitive plate ready to take whatever print you want to put on it—We have no art, no manners, no intellect—we have nothing. We water at the eyes at our own stupidity. We have only mass movement like a sea. . . . Ugliness is a horror to me but it is less abhorrent than to be like you [Europe] in the most remote, the most minute particular. For the moment I hate you, I hate your orchestras, your libraries, your sciences, your yearly salons, your finely tuned intelligences of all sorts. My intelligence is as finely tuned as yours but it lives in hell . . .

It is this unrelieved quality in American life that the best American fiction does, indeed, relieve. It occurs, it is surely clear, in few novels, and these often berated, misjudged, or ignored, e.g., Edward Dahlberg's *Bottom Dogs,* William Eastlake's *The Bronc People,* Paul Goodman's *The Grand Piano,* Douglas Woolf's *Wall to Wall,* Robert Creeley's *The Island,* John Hawkes' *The Beetle Leg,* and Paul Bowles' *The Sheltering Sky.* Williams, in his *Autobiography,* speaks of "the inarticulate patient" who "struggles to lay himself bare for you, or with nothing more than a boil on his back is so caught off balance that he reveals some secret twist of a whole community's pathetic way of thought . . ." The Stecher trilogy is a work of fiction that catches, off balance, by the most precise and deliberate accrual of those "isolate flecks," an entire American family over a twenty-year span, revealing it as well as the particularly American world in which it at once prospers and is subtly defeated.

THE PROSE of the Stecher trilogy seems remote from that in Williams' earlier imaginative prose works, *Kora in Hell, Spring and All, The Great American Novel, The Descent of Winter,* and *A Novelette,* all of which are almost gorgeous in their marshaling of expressionist and surrealist prose techniques taken from modern French literature.

The same contrast may be noted in the verse, the earlier
being packed and convoluted and microcosmically meta-
phoric, and the latter, as in *Journey to Love*, having the
complete mastery of statement which can dispose of all
trope and convention, and register the subtlest nuances
effortlessly, and in language so "plain" as to defy analysis
as to the magic of its power.

It was Williams who first signaled the death of imagism,
who broke the ground for the discarding of simile and
contrast, who insisted on a verse that would be neither
qualitatively measurable nor "free." Contemporary American poetry—I mean the kind that has added an integer or
facet to the poetic process, not the kind that scholar-critics
like to call "major poetry"—has, as everyone knows, moved
away from the image at bewildering speed, and has completely done away with simile; even metaphor has become
a manifestation of the whole structure of the poem, not
one of the components of the engine that makes it go.
Jack Spicer, I would say, has shown us most clearly how
this poem may be made to work, but it was Williams who
wrote the poems from which Spicer proceeded, his "Portrait of a Lady," written in 1920, signaling a whole new
methodology in the writing of American verse. It was
Williams who demonstrated that if one writes the word
"glass" or "sky" or "rose," one has made an "image." Until
this, and its formal ramifications are understood, nothing
written about current nonacademic American poetry will
be clear or even worth attending.

It was the long period of trial and error in the composition of his verse that brought to Williams his prose style,
a style that, in the Stecher trilogy, defies mining, i.e., there
is *nothing* beneath the surface of the words. Williams
specifically applied himself to the composition of a prose
that functions only as paint functions in a canvas. A conventional narrative is also avoided, so that one has not
even a progression of events to deal with; there are no
climaxes, no denouement, no tragedy. What does *White
Mule* mean? Read it. The signals are missing. The young
Stecher family, Joe, Gurlie, Lottie, and the newborn Flossie,
does things that cry out for "treatment": at the beginning
of the novel, Lottie, when shown her baby sister for the

first time, says, "the nasty thing," and slaps her with all her strength in the face. What does this mean about Lottie, and the relationship she will have with her sister? Is it possible that Williams will not *use* it to construct a tale of sibling rivalry that can extend throughout the trilogy? He does not. Then it must simply be a "slice of life," a hunk of good old realism from the provincial doctor. What this slap does is show us a facet of Lottie's *mother,* Gurlie. This is done without comment; look for yourself.

It is a flash of the actual. Coupled with many others, it makes the novel. This is Flossie's book; with her birth the Stecher family begins its move toward success and its attendant and almost inarticulate loss, its ordered move, one might say, toward order: underneath which there is the subtlest aroma of sadness and meaninglessness. But never, never tragedy. There is no tragedy in America, there is only that state described by the American phrase "washed up." The nearest we get to tragedy is the situation so precisely limned in *The Great Gatsby,* which, if it be tragic, is so in the most picayune sense, lacking nobility, grace, and founded on the triple American flaws of greed, carelessness, and romantic nostalgia.

We are dull and torpid, and because of this look for writers to tell us that these states are tragic, romantically heroic, that our lives are *gloriously* blasted from the start, that our defeats *mean* something, i.e., in some transcendental way. We adore losing the way that Frank Sinatra loses in his songs, but we cannot stomach the loss that Williams speaks of. Our representative fiction is romantic because the natural state of American life is featurelessness; we must give it a face—any face. Who is our ranking official great novelist? Mailer, of course, who else can it be?—a writer who has never written a first-class novel, a man who cannot refrain (he is a supreme Romantic) from putting a coat of paint on everything he sees, so that his America is unrecognizable to anyone who has walked the street. His imagination functions in a world of ideas, which may be why the novel has become almost impossible for him to write—witness his last two attempts. In his novels, tragedy is sexual violence, his heroes lose, and in losing win—something. The Medal of Romantic Wisdom, perhaps.

202 NEW AMERICAN REVIEW

But American life is not tragic, it is dull; its losses are almost silent, inexpressible, obscure. Williams tells us this, and tells us with such persistence, that we cannot stand him. We will not stand him. The imagination, only the imagination can release us from despair? Who will believe it? We need signals; evil must be given a face or else we will be forced to accept the fact that it has no face, that our corruption is diluted so thoroughly that we all have a little in us, like strontium-90.

Gurlie is a willful woman who nags her husband, Joe, into success because she wants to be rich. What else is America good for? she says. What else, indeed? She succeeds, and by the end of the trilogy, in *The Build-Up*, Joe does not even offer her token resistance. Gurlie is a "bitch," the upwardly mobile, conniving, and mindless wife who pushes her sensitive husband until he is, indeed, rich. So there is your American novel—or is it? What has Williams done with it? Where are those signals we look for when we meet the fictional bitch? They grow old together, they have even been *happy* together. The novel makes no sense! It has no plot! What are we to do with this woman who has tricked us? Nothing happens, nothing *really* happens! It is not even an attack on the middle class, it is—nothing. Under the words there is nothing. It is American success as it is, without tragedy, without grace or understanding.

> as if the earth under our feet
> were
> an excrement of some sky
>
> and we degraded prisoners
> destined
> to hunger until we eat filth
>
> while the imagination strains
> after deer
> going by fields of goldenrod in
>
> the stifling heat of September
> Somehow
> it seems to destroy us

—Williams says, in "To Elsie." And ends this great lyric:

                no one
                to witness
                and adjust, no one to drive the car

Except for the artist and his relentless and despised imagination.

IN "WHITE MULE," published in 1937, in the midst of a
deluge of socially relevant fiction perhaps unmatched for
sentimentality and bathos until our own time, Williams
chronicles, as I have said, the first year of life of the baby,
Flossie Stecher, and her parents' initial move toward success: a curiously detached thing to be doing at a time when
more admired and certainly more famous writers were
contributing to the building of the brave new society in
which we are, of course, now living. We read these writers
now with the same curiosity with which we read back
issues of popular magazines of the time; they are more
remote from us than are Baudelaire or Sterne. (Some of
Williams' peers—equally detached—have by now earned
their deserved praise: West, Fitzgerald, Djuna Barnes,
et al. But Williams' fiction is still largely unknown.) He
might well have been better employed at slicing up some
life for us, or making us indignant; he did neither. What
he did do, we can now see, was to show us where the
thirties came from (and the sixties and seventies as well),
and why. The novels take us up to the First World War,
and the Stechers' triumph—and defeat. They are bewildered as to the hidden nature of their defeat; they really
do not know that they have been defeated.

It is this inarticulateness, this bewilderment in the face
of success that has always been so specifically American,
so that novels that detail the journey "from rags to riches"
must need be, so it seems, novels that have a dimension
that we can grasp: the loss and the destruction inherent
in American success must be made manifest in tragedy or
protest, polemic or satire, so that we may trace the figure
of decline. Williams chose a way to trace this decline that
has made him, I believe, almost wholly misunderstood.
He came to see that despair and defeat are indigenous
and that for us, the tragic is exotic. There was no language

for the revelation of that strange mélange of prosperity and bitterness that Williams found in his own small-town life, and it was this search for a language fit to express it that dictated the composition of his trilogy.

As I have suggested, the "theme" of almost all serious American fiction of the past forty years is romantic loss. Let me go further and say that this loss is almost always redeemed because we insist on imputing to the losers the knowledge of their own heroic pathos. From Jake Barnes to Stephen Rojack, we see the heroic pattern clear. But what can we do with that rarest American fiction that details the defeat that is neither "principled" nor even understood to *be* defeat? How, even, is such fiction written? It is still a novelist's problem; in Williams' time, it was the problem entire, since the "little man" in much of the fiction contemporaneous with his own was a sentimental figure understandable only as a victim of abstract powers of government, business, prejudice, politics, destiny, etc. Williams had no relation to those writers whose characters are manipulated by "history," nor was he in any way akin to those who offered figures whose ostensible success masked ravaged psyches. He was interested in the successful character, the "nice guy" whose life was, on the whole, placid and stable, and whose imaginative life was atrophied or dead. He insisted on revealing defeat not in the guise of success, but as an inextricable part of it—and hence, totally obscured. His novels are barely plotted, his characters flat and ordinary, the destruction of their hopes a whisper. These things were all necessary to the realization of his intent, and he had no models.

His problem was not that the patterns of American life were unobservable but that a language had to be found to express them, an American language. Williams' well-known attack upon Eliot is understandable only if we know that he refused not his gifts but his Europeanized mind; it was this belief in a native art that makes clear what he meant when he wrote, "Your attention is called now and then to some beautiful line or sonnet sequence because of what is said there. So be it. To me all sonnets say the same thing of no importance"; we see what he meant when he said that this American language came from "the mouths of Polish mothers." The dumb quality of our malaise had to be given a voice, a "redeeming language" had to be found that would enable an American to discover, in literature, the "secret twist" that reveals a community.

It may well be that the waste and violence and loss in American life is partially accounted for by the fact that we cannot assuage our miseries, no matter the floods of "hard information" daily tendered us. We know everything, and nothing. We are wild in our dullness, our inability to *do* anything in the face of this endless stream of news that irritates us without respite. We look for our relief in the products of the imagination, but we have no heroes except the romantic losers. When that "secret spring of all our lives" is tapped, as it is in Williams' trilogy, it is difficult for us to accept it, since it is difficult for us to accept the truth that our lives make a pattern no more meaningful than its own shape. "No figures, no forms, no known largenesses whatsoever. Zero."

The Stecher trilogy shows us that a family can be defeated in its success and still have a reasonably contented life; at the same time, the Stecher family is revelatory of that larger suburban community that has, in recent years, become an American cliché. Williams explored it when it was in its infancy, and explored it without moralizing, without a point of view, except that, exactly: a point of *view*. Williams sees, and his observation is carried over to us by his voice, an American voice, emerging from a characteristically staid and placid hell, but one in which we are all, nevertheless, burning.

LOUIS ZUKOFSKY, writing in 1930 of Williams' early collections of poems, notes that "there are poems that will stay though many lines are invalidated by his [Williams'] subsequent criticism. It is salutary that these lines may be omitted and still leave a number of structures. The process of rehabilitating the good to its rightful structure is always possible with writing in which something was seen, a quantity heard, an emotion apprehended to begin with." And Williams, writing in *Kora in Hell*, says: "Often a poem will have merit because of some one line or even one meritorious word. So it hangs heavily on its stem but still secure, the tree unwilling to release it."

It is helpful to bear these comments in mind when reading the Stecher trilogy, or, for that matter, any of Williams' work, for he was a hurried man, an overworked doctor with a wife and family, who wrote almost continually, in his office, at home, on pads in his car while going from one patient to another. There is much in his work that can be "invalidated" by his own "subsequent criticism": his alternative to writing in this fashion was not to write at all. It was the necessity to write within the harshly defined limits of his own life that somehow drove his style through the tangle of accepted niceties and made it immediate; it was this reliance on the actual, on the power of sight as against "intellect"—his works written in white heat and polished later—that has made so many people speak of him as an imagist. But the "images" are *actual*, redeemed by the careful composition of the words so that they are not "literary," and they are not photographic.

> By the road to the contagious hospital
> under the surge of the blue
> mottled clouds driven from the
> northeast . . .

Those lines betoken the demise of imagism.

To catch the whole of his world on the wing, to be its sensory apparatus, and then to compose these impressions so that they would stand free, each to itself, remote, remote from the search for the image that is addition, and *not* what he wanted. He wanted total clarification, a language to catch and hold fast the flat surfaces of the life that surrounded him daily. "That which had been impossible for him at first had become possible. Everything had been removed that other men had tied to the words to secure them to themselves. Clean, clean, he had taken each word and made it new for himself so that at last it was new, free from the world for himself . . ." Williams wrote that in *The Great American Novel*. Free from the banal, the formulated, all signals discarded, the Stecher trilogy justifies this early note—"everything . . . removed that other men had tied to the words . . ."

Postscript

As far as the writing itself is concerned it takes next to no time at all. Much too much is written every day of our lives. We are overwhelmed by it. But when at times we see through the welter of evasive or interested patter, when by chance we penetrate to some moving detail of a life, there is always time to bang out a few pages. The thing isn't to find the time for it—we waste hours every day doing absolutely nothing at all—the difficulty is to catch the evasive life of the thing, to phrase the words in such a way that stereotype will yield a moment of insight. That is where the difficulty lies. We are lucky when that underground current can be tapped and the secret spring of all our lives will send up its pure water. It seldom happens. A thousand trivialities push themselves to the front, our lying habits of everyday speech and thought are foremost, telling us that *that* is what "they" want to hear. Tell them something else.

—*The Autobiography of William Carlos Williams*

No outside program has influenced his social awareness. It is the product of the singular creature living in society and expressing in spite of the numb terror around him the awareness which after a while cannot help but be general. It is the living creature becoming conscious of his own needs through the destruction of the various isolated around him, and till his day comes continuing unwitnessed to work, no one but himself to drive the car through the suburbs, till they too become conscious of demands unsatisfied by the routine senseless repetition of events.

—Louis Zukofsky (1930)

Escalator

Patricia Goedicke

MEETING me it was love at first sight:
You named me for my aspirations.

Ascending with me like a serpent's tongue
Into the one heaven of a department store

You called me water flowing uphill
As smooth, as calm

One foot sliding into
The other and that one
Into the next and so

On like a caterpillar unfolding
On bird's feet, precise
Liquid

Jeweled belt going up
Yes truly I am a dream machine
Riding me no one speaks

Electric
Noise bubbles and boils

Like the tubes of a Moog Synthesizer
Yards and yards of me coil
From the basement to the mezzanine

Expanding, contracting, in paradise
Like a zipper silently opening

Up again, down again, smooth
In slow motion hunted

As you, lordly, rise
Without moving hand or foot
Past everything you ever wanted.

From an Epistolary Sequence

Bill Henkin

THE fish in the sea, the birds in the sky, the rats
in the ghettos, and you, and I—what have we
in common besides a name, and the fact that we live?

Every third day I take out my scissors
and cut another square inch from your picture.
By my calculations, in a year
there'll be nothing left of you but hair
and perhaps an ear. How is Marrakesh?
Is hashish as cheap there as my love was here?

§

Dear Clayton: I wanted to explain
that anger and hatred are different things
and that I loved you, in my broken way.
Otherwise, I wouldn't have sent you my hand.

Since, though, you returned it in a week
I'm sending my nose, mouth and eyes.
There's no place we can meet. I'm facing that.

§

You're in training to become a parachute.
This is no mean exercise for a child
much less an adult. You must be nimble
and courageous as a lobster stepping off
some vast oceanic shelf. You may die

or else return eons from now, a deep
sea monster, miles long and vicious.
You may come back tomorrow as yourself
open as a sail, let down easy.

§

The fourth planet from the Sun is Earth.
Or no, the third. The fourth is Mars where
there's little water and the nights are colder than ice.
It seems men couldn't live there in peace or at war.

That's all I know about astronomy.
If you need to know more, lie on your back at night
in an open field and make up constellations.

§

The book's in Spanish, the title's in French, and I'm in
deep with your imagery. Why do you speak
of tarantulas as if they were snakes? Why do you call
warm orange? Why do you never call
me by name when all your poems refer
to me? Sitting on a park bench
reading this dustjacket with your name and picture
I'm surprised you didn't become a lawyer.
It says here you started law school
but dropped out to become yourself. What does that
    mean?
Who were you all the years you held my cock
calling me *Mon petit, mon droit, ma discipline?*

In Search of a Missing IUD

Anne Higgins

Dear Dr. Lunt,

You remember the other day when you had me trussed up on the examining table like a chicken and told me for my own reassurance, peace of mind I think you said, that I should have an abdominal X ray made; that you would write the instruction on a slip of paper: "For the presence of a missing IUD," to be handed to the X-ray man . . .? It struck me then, as now, as a comic line. I wonder that you didn't see the humor of it. I suppose in your line of work these little physical ironies cease to be funny. Or maybe you simply deem it more politic not to snicker at your patients' dilemmas, at least not in front of them.

To sidetrack a little bit, because I've never had the courage to ask directly, what makes a man decide on an Ob-Gyn specialty? I can't help but think that as a day-by-day way of making one's living it must be a bore. To peer at nothing but the hind quarters of trussed-up women. *Chacun à son goût,* I suppose. Still. My apologies for getting personal, but remember that you asked a great many personal questions of me and on the strength of my answers made a great many personal comments and judgments. I must confess that I was rather offended by the whole interview, however professionally motivated your questions and well intended your advice. I suppose it's nothing more than a matter of pride—I have an MA in English and a PhD in Comparative Literature—and I do hate to be talked down to. (You wouldn't have expected a PhD in Comp Lit to have ended a sentence with a preposition, would you. To down hate to be talked?) Frankly you sounded like the Doctor's Advice column out of *Redbook* magazine. And I must say that your hands are unusually small. I'm not being indelicate and I'm sure that you know what you're doing, but analogously speaking, would you expect an extremely short-fingered man to go into concert-piano work? What I'm trying to say is, is it possible that you're hampered professionally by your small hands? Personally speaking, is it possible that you missed something you would otherwise have found had you been more generously endowed? Manually, that is. Look, the fact of the matter is, bluntly, this: you thought, via your probe instruments and look-see devices that the IUD was still there but you couldn't find the nylon strings that would indicate its presence to you. Now: if you think the IUD is still there then where could the nylon strings have gone? Surely they're not wafting around up there in sub-uterine breezes. All right, I'll have the X ray made to make sure of what's where. But the reason I went to you in the first place was to avoid just such an ambiguous mess as this. I have no professional quarrel with you, but at this point I do wonder about the possible professional handicap of your hands.

Dear Father Zimmel,

Just a quick note from a former student of yours. You may remember that I took your adult theology courses off and on for five years. I was that striving, conscientious woman in the back of the room who beleaguered your life for so many years. Your eyes would shine with Holy Spirited light as you put the one of little faith in her proper place: i.e., down. Oh I know you, Father, you can't deny your venomous delight, your wicked pride in your debating skills. (Was it a subject for confession, this theological hubris?) But I know myself too, a pseudo-student of Voltaire and Diderot, a one-time admirer of Plato's Philosopher-King, a long-time disciple of Marx the Idealist, a camp follower of Dorothy Day, an early devotee of Teilhard de Chardin (did *you* ever get through him? Ah, gotcha!), an enthusiast at the same time of Catherine the Great, Hamilton, Jefferson, Walt Whitman, Ezra Pound, Henry Miller, Thérèse the Little Flower, Genet, Bertrand Russell, Dietrich Bonhoeffer, *yes* to Meister Eckhart, Phyllis

McGinley, and Betty Friedan. Paradoxes, paradoxes. And guilty of rationalizations, neuroses. I never got anywhere with any of them; unlike John the Baptist I was a reed shaken by every wind, swayed from right to left depending on the suasiveness of the breeze. How I used to pore over those books and pamphlets on the Church as Magister, the pronouncements on authority and obedience, the summonses to the logic and truth of Natural Law. In spite of them and your eloquence I remained unconvinced. Married to a Catholic, I practiced the precepts of the Church. (I'm sure you remember me now: I was that lady who was *always* pregnant.) On my own I decided to summon a different natural law into account: the one concerned with the point of diminishing returns. You would consider yourself justified in a good theologically sneering belly laugh. God is not mocked, His Law will not be abrogated by the libertine advances of twentieth-century science. Madam, I can hear you thunder, do you understand now that the Hound of Heaven will pursue you into every wickedly free-thinking gynecologist's office that you enter?

Well, Father, what is at stake? The Pascalian Wager? What it boils down to is this: candy is dandy but nothing at all would be safer. Galilean, thou hast conquered.

Dear Sister Seraphim,

I've been meaning to write for months, to tell you how much I enjoyed seeing you again; and really how impressed I am at the changes that have taken place in the last fifteen years. Nuns certainly have become swingers, haven't they? No more of those ridiculous social censures (you probably don't remember, but I do, that I spent my whole last senior semester campused as a punitive result of my contempt of those censures); full-fledged departments now in soc., psych., and poli sci.; a mixed drama department, taking advantage of nearby men's colleges (didn't you—honestly now—want to writhe at the sight of girls playing Lear and Othello?); Saul Alinsky and Paul Goodman invited to speak on campus. No administrative pronouncements on the proper length of skirts . . . Talk about progress!

Could I interject here that nineteen years ago, when I was in your freshman philosophy class, you gave one of the most brilliant lectures I've ever heard, on Augustine's concept of time. All these years and I've never told you. Ah, sins of omission.

One jarring note: it disturbed me—it bugged me, if you want to know the truth—that you referred to Alinsky as "a smart Jew." Really, I felt that was beneath you; certainly it was hitting below the ecumenical belt. I've often wondered since whether it slipped out as a remnant of pre-ecumenical indoctrination or whether you cast it out as a barb to me. At any rate I didn't challenge it, I let it pass. I should have said something. But a first meeting in fifteen years . . . one tends to be polite, one is awed by the passage of time. And plain old nostalgia. Anyway, for the record, I object to stereotypes. Particularly, you middle-class-lace-curtain-Irish nun you, ones that refer to Jews.

One more thing for the record: if it appears in the Alumnae News that Mrs. Michael Callahan, nee Leslie Goldman, wife of the successful Omaha attorney and busy mother of eight visited St. Rose's over the holidays and had a nice long chat with Sr. Seraphim . . . boom! There goes my annual contribution. I can see it now: "Leslie Callahan, who incidentally holds a graduate degree, is a shining example of the Educated Catholic (sic) Woman we try to turn out here at St. Rose's. Welcoming each new bundle of joy as they appear in annual succession, Leslie realizes the tremendous advantages of her educational background as a guide for teaching and nourishing these tender souls entrusted by God to her care. As she told Sr. Seraphim . . ."

Well, I won't have it. I was long gone from St. Rose's, and immersed in (and rather exhausted by) an arduous process of "finding myself" at Columbia . . . when along came Mike Callahan, that handsome Irish charmer with glittering teeth and eyes burning blue pockets of salvation and ambition. Save me from myself, would Mike Callahan. Redeem the Left-wing Jewess. Impose order on anarchy, truelove on falsesex. What could be more seductive? I fell hard and fast, swept off my feet by the passion of chaste kisses. Who needed a career, a sterile PhD, when Love beckoned in the marriage bed behind the altar? I took all the pre-Cana courses, signed everything, all the dotted lines everywhere. Sewed up everything tight. Including myself. And little heaven-sent Callahans appeared with the regularity that other women get their periods. Of course I love my children, and Mike is generous about providing a weekly cleaning woman, a personal allowance, and so on. That point is: what's the point? What's the point of enshrining a fertile woman? Fertility, like rain in season, is easy to come by. One prays against droughts but against floods too. If one prays at all and/or has any common sense. At any rate the Callahans—Successful Corporation Lawyer Michael Callahan and His Lovely Family —appear regularly in the Omaha press. Mrs. Callahan is expecting her third child, her fifth, her seventh, her eighth. The fantastic Mrs. Callahan has just given birth to her thirty-fourth child. Mrs. Callahan, in spite of her busy schedule, finds time for community work, is active in many charitable and social organizations, and is on the board of the Omaha Arts and Culture Program. Mr. Callahan is an outstanding Catholic layman, well known in the business community, leader of the Anti-Smut Campaign, "a dabbler," he laughs modestly, "in politics," and twice voted Mr. Omaha by the Omaha Chamber of Commerce.

Dear Sister Seraphim, do you realize that some of the priests we have over for dinner are still disgruntled over the introduction of lay participation in the Mass? That Mike and I didn't speak to each other for three months before the last election? That Mike Callahan, that outstanding Catholic layman-lawyer—and *here's* a choice bit of *sub rosa* gossip for you—contributed fifteen hundred dollars toward the purchase of a neighboring house, in a nonexistent family's name, in order that it wouldn't be purchased by "undesirable elements" (read: a Negro dentist and his family).

Well. Greetings from Omaha. I didn't intend this to be so personal. I understand there are great changes going on which have not yet hit this acreage of the universe. Blessings on you and forge ahead! It was nice to be East again and to see you after so long, even under the circumstances. P.S. My late father used to ponder—with sly humor—why so many nuns took the names of male saints: Sr. Mary Michael, Sr. Francis, Sr. Paul, Sr. William Marie, etc. Frankly, if you want to know my honest opinion, I can't see names like Sr. Celestine, Sr. Illuminata, Sr. Immaculata, or Sr. Seraphim either. P.P.S. I'm sure Father, wherever he is, thanks you for your prayers. He was a secularist most of his life but he was a *good* man.

Dear Mr. Herzog,

I'll get right to the point: *don't* settle for Ramona. I know you have your needs, your faults, your weaknesses like everybody else, but the more I think about the possibility of that liaison, the more I think it would be a bad mistake. A really bad mistake. You know what would happen, she'd sap your creativity in a wink. No, no, that's wrong. Gradually. You wouldn't even realize it was happening until you found yourself so thoroughly attuned to Food, to Culture, to Ramona's Orphic rites that you would never even have the desire to take up your pen again, never mind the strength. You would complain, only once, and only of a very slight headache, and there would be Ramona: "Oh no, Moses darling, don't tire yourself. Rest now." Perhaps she would put on Egyptian music to soothe you—though I have more than the suspicion that after a while the Egyptian stuff would go, you'd be getting Mantovani, don't kid yourself. Remember that Ramona is in her late thirties and that these exotic binges become tiresome, they're *wearing* on a woman that age. Ramona too will be getting headaches, but not slight ones. Huge ones. And then there will be lowered blinds and vinegar cloths for her forehead; no music at all, not even Mantovani. But for the present Ramona will soothe you, comfort you, build up your still undernourished ego. Ramona understands everything, anticipates your every desire. After a while you will want to put your *own* sugar in your coffee. You think you will scream if you hear the sympathetic assent of "poor Moses" one more time. (And you will feel guilty about that precisely because Ramona *is* a dear, good woman and undoubtedly she *does* love you and want your happiness.) But for right now, Ramona will put on her clanging Egyptian music—oh yes, I've heard those sensuous wails—and dance tenderly naked for you, clad only in Vita Dew Youth Emulsion, jingling jangling gold bracelets and her black lace underpants. (Panties to women like Ramona.) Oh God, and the high heels of course.

Moses, that's the crux: don't marry a woman who Prepares herself. At thirty-seven or so she's a looker still with superb shoulders and good breasts—and by your own admission the shape of a woman's breasts is important to you (as appalling a weakness as I find that to be in you, still it's honest, it's an honest weakness)—but think, Moses, think that when Ramona is forty-seven and her whole life is a dedicated, consuming passion to keeping those shoulders soft, that bosom high and firm, those Orphic elements trim. Hours, whole days will be spent Preparing herself. At sixty, after a month of grim, self-disciplined Preparations, she will still be standing coyly in the bedroom door (the bedroom lighting will have been rearranged to forbid harshness at any hour) and asking, "Moses darling, do I please you?" *That* is what will become of your life, you a domesticated poodle leafing through Ramona's magazines, waiting for the mistress to appear, in order to give a few appreciative barks (quacks, the old quack-quack phenomenon, as you so well described it) and be led, sniffing tamely and with an increasing exhaustion, through the hoops of the Orphic rituals.

I sound shrill. Perhaps I am simply jealous of Ramona. Ramona, after all, is a woman of the world, perfumed, a cooker of fancy shrimp and arbiter of dry wines. She has the good sense to serve chilled grapes for dessert and not strawberry shortcake; she attends lectures and is sexually mature. (I suppose I hate her because she's a realist at heart as well as a narcissist.) Certainly Ramona regards Precautions as a necessary part of Preparations. Ramona knew that when she was sixteen. How do some women know all about these things and manage them successfully? I assure you that other women are not so fortunate in these affairs.

At any rate, I beg you not to marry Ramona. I feel no immodesty about proposing myself; on the other hand, no shame, only a little sadness knowing you wouldn't have me. I used to be one of those dungareed, flat-chested, hawk-nosed beauties that are prone to prowl around Eastern universities talking literature and art in coffee houses and crummy pubs. After eight children I am still flat-chested and hawk-nosed but I have acquired a mid-aged, mid-west spread. They like wide-hipped women out here; their greatest compliment is to ask if you are a local girl. Wealthy Nebraskan businessmen would overlook (forgive!) my Semitic nose for the pleasure of my heavy thighs. Faagh, I look down my fine curved beak at them. Go eat corn, man, you and I could make no good music together. On the other hand, I see myself clearly on the Ludeyville wavelength, attuned to your marvelous old place up there, running green through the summers, crouching low by fires in winter. The acreage, the solitude, the physical work involved in keeping up a place like that: bliss. Just that. Real work pleasures, like driving nails into hard wood and bringing an abandoned garden to ordered life. My husband calls the carpenter, the plumber, the electrician. Appliances whir softly, constantly. Things that go whir in the night. How blissful the silence of the Berkshires. How divine a stove that didn't blind you with chrome! I could be happy in Ludeyville. I repeat without shame, I could make you happy. No go, eh? Moses in the fullness of his Jewish heart may love children, but not eight little Callahans and their wide-hipped Omaha ma. I don't blame you for a minute, it's a preposterous idea.

I didn't start out intending this proposal at all. I started out giving you a little piece of well-meant advice on Ramona, which I will now (tiresomely) repeat and for the last time: don't do it. The temptation is great. But dear Moses Herzog, you are too close to sainthood to give it up now for a few years of mortal happiness. The end. And anyway you probably wouldn't even be that happy.

Dear Gypsy,

Remember that time you and Jon were living in Lima and you got stoned on pisco sours one afternoon and the Terrible Thing happened? After four years I still giggle thinking about it. There you were, smashed as could be, and in desperation hanging your head over the toilet when Jon comes staggering in, cross-eyed drunk, and says, "Gypsy darling, let me help you" and *drops the toilet seat on your nose.* I'm laughing now, just at the thought of that letter. You thought for sure your nose was broken, the poor bridge was bent all out of shape and it swelled immediately and turned seven shades of green and purple and you had dinner guests that night. And you couldn't say a word. As I remember, you made some feeble excuse about bumping into a doorway in the middle of the night, and everyone thought Jon had beaten you up and exchanged raised eyebrows over the dinner candles. You couldn't even write to anyone about it, except me. That always struck me as the funniest part, not being able to explain it. How can you say: my throbbing nose is big as a potato because my husband dropped the toilet seat on it. It's like suffering from hemorrhoids. You can complain in company about a migraine headache, about having cancer, ulcers, sinusitis, arthritis, neuralgia, neuritis. But you *can't* writhe on the edge of your chair and moan Oh my aching ass!

Which brings me to the point of this letter. To whom else could I write about this comedy of the absurd? Remember at Father's funeral when you advised me that if I didn't want to go on proliferating like a rabbit I Should Do Something About It? Well, I did. I went to the most discreet gynecologist in town and got one of those squiggly loop-de-loops. And you know what's happened to it? I don't either. Neither does the Gyn. Maybe it's there, maybe it's not. I'm supposed to go get an X ray to find out. What's Mike going to say when he gets a bill for one flat abdominal X-ray plate? I can always pay cash, that's not the real problem. It's simply the psychological effect it has on me. Frankly, at this point I feel like a damned sneak. I don't agree with Mike, I think he's all wrong on a lot of issues, but there's a certain basic honesty and integrity that must be preserved in a marriage if it's going to work at all. It was bad enough having to sneak to the Gyn, but now this sneaking off to the X-ray man . . . where did I read once that guilty people get caught because they have a subconscious *need* to get caught? I feel like the unholy alliance of Freud and the Catholic church has teamed up, in a spurt of black humor, to get me. (Good grief, not only guilt but paranoia. What next?) Mike is simply intransigent on the whole issue. He was furious with me even for talking to the priest to get "permission" to use the Pill (if I never read another article or listen to another discussion on Morality and the Pill I'll die happy). His final words (cold, but concessive) (for him) were that if I wanted to take The Pill (why do they always capitalize it, like some divinity or higher institution) he wouldn't object, though he certainly didn't approve of "thwarting Nature" like that. (When he had that kidney operation last year he darn well had an anesthetic and I didn't hear any objections *then* about "thwarting Nature.") Anyway, it was at that point I decided *I* didn't want to take the Pill. Talk about interfering with Nature! Why should I let my body chemistry and whole hormone system get thrown out of whack. So off I sneaked to the loop-de-loop man and only to have the Final Solution turn out like this.

What's really funny about it is that the whole thing is right out of a best-seller. Some Mary McCarthy character would get herself in a situation like this. The girl goes to the clinic and gets her device. Three months later she goes back for the routine checkup and they can't find it. Trauma. She comes home, expecting her boyfriend to take her in his arms and say something consoling like, "Never mind, love, we'll find another one." Instead, bored by her hysterics and uninterested in the femaleness of the problem anyway, he is crass, callow. He finally says something really boorish, like, "What do you expect me to do? Send up a search party?" The girl sobs, rages. She accuses him of not loving her and by then she is right, he doesn't, he couldn't care less. He takes up painting and hashish again, and she goes home to Mother. There's even material here for a television script, one of those deadly family situation comedies. Outline: everyone loses something and finds it again. Junior's lost dog finds its way home (accompanied, of course, by a litter of pups—cute!), Sister discovers the lost Atlantis (in the encyclopedia—educational!), Pop finds his misplaced pipe on the roof (hilarious!—American Pops are such sweet, inept bunglers), Mom discovers her missing IUD (in the garden? *in the asparagus patch?* We just lost the sponsor), and Grandma finds the lost chord. Sound of a great Amen as the camera pans to a long shot of the mountains.

Dear oh dear, Gypsy, how did identical twins ever turn out so different as we? You still barren after three marriages and I caught up on the proverbial horns over this idiotic birth-control business. I know your childlessness is a source of great sorrow to you but truly, Gypsy, I couldn't hand over even one of my children, not even to you who I know would love it dearly and spoil it rotten. (I'm still not sure whether when I saw you at the funeral you were serious or facetious about that proposal.) I'm a neurotic and at times a crappy mother but I have this *thing* about my kids. On the other hand, I often envy (read: turn pea-green with frustrated jealousy) your freedom to travel, to indulge your artistic and intellectual caprices, to meet the Beautiful *and* the Interesting People! (*We* are on a *tu-toi* basis with the chairman of the State Republican Club. Oh, we are *Important* People!) I could even get interested in politics—if politics were the subject at hand and not wheeler-dealer political games. These disgusting exhibitions of avarice and cynicism which we entertain in our living room are what are known as grassroots politics. Hear my cries of disavowal . . . And yet what am *I* contributing to the Betterment of Mankind? Well. More later.

Dear Father,

I've just been writing to Gypsy and wondering how the two of us, she and I, managed to turn out so unalike. But now I am thinking, No, we're not really that much different. The real mystery here is how you managed to turn out two who are so different from *you*. Also, I was writing to Sr. Seraphim and ended up with some inane postscript defending you as a "good man." I don't know why. I suppose it has something to do with the old De Mortuis etc. theme. And in the conversation I had with Sr. S. when I went to see her after the funeral, I laid it on quite a bit thicker than merely a good man. I made you out to be one of those heart-of-gold humanists; Father, forgive me, I had you embracing Orthodoxy at the very end, and not only buried with your *tallis* in the casket but facing toward Zion with a little sack of Israeli soil under your head. I don't know what got into me. I suppose maybe I just wanted to one-up her with religion. I can hear you rattling your coffin with laughter. Even worse, and this will really tickle you, she fell for it. The only thing that would have impressed her more would have been a deathbed conversion to Catholicism. However, the Orthodoxy bit was quite dramatically correct. I conjured pictures of Yahrzeit lights and keening relatives rending their garments . . . I'm not proud of myself. I suppose deep down I always wanted you to be exactly that sort of man who would have a funeral like that.

When I was growing up—and Gypsy too—we craved the identity that other kids had. They rebelled against their immigrant parents or grandparents, when they went to college they had nose jobs done and pretended not to understand Yiddish, but Father, we were steeped in European readings, how we wanted you to grow a long patriarchal beard, to strap on phylacteries and sit swaying and wailing and muttering ancient prayers and incantations. How we used to hope that one of your silvery-laughed lady friends would turn out to be a Jewish mama and light the candles on Friday nights. Your funeral, by the way, was filled with these ladies, aging now but heavily mascaraed, all with lacquered hair, both young and old—both men and women too, yes, Father, they all turned out—all trilling in their thrilling theatrical voices, a regular chapelful of preening peacocks. I think half of them came to meet their agents. If it's any comfort to you it was a grand affair. The embarrassed rabbi, worldly fellow though he was, broke out in a bad case of hives. He was assisted by a nondenominational minister whose chief claim to fame is that he once officiated at the marriage of a homosexual pair in an East Village apartment; his homily on tolerance is still widely remembered. The funeral cortege was a status admixture of limousines and roaring Hondas: who could be farther In or farther Out. At the final chapel service several ladies fainted from the heat, and Gypsy's purse got snatched. Wild. It was right up your alley.

Gypsy and I didn't think it was very funny. Gypsy, in fact, became so enraged at the oleaginous minister that she threatened to report him to the Better Business Bureau. (That *did* strike me as funny but she wouldn't laugh about it even later.)

I'm thinking that the reason "good man" sticks in my craw was not anything to do with your succession of ladies —though by what quirk of paternal tenderness did you keep them hidden from Gypsy and me for so long?—but with your diabolical refusal to make any judgments except as they concerned pleasure. You didn't mix the sacred and the profane, you refused to acknowledge any distinction. Thus you were not a bad man or a good man but a neuter neutral laughing man. I'm convinced that the only reason you honored that absurd deathbed wish of Mother's to send one of us to a Baptist and the other to a Catholic college was because you found it so outrageously funny. Ethical Culture Mother's half-Jewish daughters separated and sent off at age seventeen to cope with the formal rigors of Christian theology. And you waving a debonair handkerchief at the train station and laughing like a madman up your agnostic sleeve. Good God, what a joke. I must hand it to you, you preceded the black humorists by forty years. You were op/pop art fleshed out. Really Father, you would have enjoyed your funeral. You knew all along you were going to die. It was your best joke, your lifetime *coup*, and with unerring sense of theater you saved it for last.

The only good thing about your funeral, really the only decent thing that happened during that whole fluttering travesty of death and burial, was a meeting I had with the Anderssons. You may not even remember them; they were Ethical Culture people, friends of Mother's. I remember meeting them several times as a child, and they were old then. Gypsy and I found them fascinating because they "talked funny." They're Scandinavian, Swedes I think. Anyway, there they were at your funeral. They had kept up with your career all these years and had come to "pay their respects." In that milling mob of self-seekers these two old humble eccentrics were like a whiff of strong ozone. Gypsy and I took them out for dinner, and here comes the story: they had no children and in their later years took to breeding and raising chihuahuas. One day, close to the lying-in time of one of the females, they spent the whole afternoon and evening away from home. Came home after midnight completely exhausted, only to find carnage all over the apartment. The female had started to whelp and was whimpering and making a mess of the living room rug; in the meantime the other dogs had gotten hold of a feather pillow from the bedroom, ripped it apart, and scattered it from one end of the apartment to the other. Feathers, mounds and heaps of feathers, wet, dry, sticky, floating, clinging feathers every place they looked, and in the midst of this the mother having pups in the middle of the living room rug. Poor weary old Anderssons, to be faced with this! Mrs. A. got a cardboard box and started assisting the mother while Mr. A. began the cleanup job. He had gathered several armloads of feathers and stuffed them in a paper bag in the kitchen when he heard a squeak. He rocked back and forth thinking he had never heard that particular floorboard squeak before. And then he realized it was coming from the paper bag and he went over and began digging through the feathers and *found* it, down in the bottom of the bag, a puppy, half smothered, still wet, and completely covered by feathers. Gently he fished it out and took it to Mrs. A. who licked it clean.

Mr. A. went on with the story but I'm stopping here. Father, *she licked it clean!* That's the point. There was nothing else to be done—such a fragile newborn couldn't be exposed to the shock of water—and without thinking twice about it she did what its mother would do. Father, I was so excited by that small incident I nearly jumped up in the restaurant and cheered. (When I told the story to Mike he was so repelled he walked out of the room.) I'm sure you never read it, but in *Kristin Lavransdatter* there was one sentence which stated simply that one of Kristin's sons had trouble with his eyes and that Kristin would clear them of matter with her tongue. Father, you understand the importance of these things, don't you? In spite of, beneath your devilish laughter you understood what it meant to be human, didn't you? To perform a human act, one of service, and in loving humility? A *Chesed shel emet?*

If you don't understand these things now I suppose you never will; not that it makes any difference. Although I must admit I would like it to make a difference.

That's about all I have to tell you right now. I'm tiring; these graphomania sieges take their toll. We're all well here, we push on from day to day. Who knows, maybe in the long run we'll find all the things we've been looking for, including our souls.

MEMO: Call Dr. Lunt's office, make an appointment. Proceed directly to the drugstore, do not pass Go, do not collect two hundred dollars. Buy arsenic. Skip Lunt, just go to the drugstore. I know the symptoms, there's no sense having Lunt confirm them. And I might end up crying in his office and then he'd have to go through his male doctor comforts his female patient routine. The old pat on the shoulder, there there buck up. Followed by the slightly impatient, "Can't you gals learn to take care of yourselves we're not in the Stone Age you know." Maybe I should just wait till the last minute and then pop over to the hospital—"There's something in my stomach, I can't imagine, do you suppose it's a gall stone?" "No, lady, it's a Mound's chocolate bar, it's a Peter Paul Almond Joy." Oh Doctor, you wit, fancy that, another bundle of almond joy.

No, I've got to see Lunt. For one thing, I've got to ask him how the baby is going to turn out. It's stupid, but I can't get over the idea that the fetus is going to form itself around the loop—sort of the way an oyster forms a pearl. Imagine a baby being born in the shape of a Lippy's loop! Or being born clutching the loop in one hand. "Nurse, do me a favor, check the kid's fists before you show him to my husband."

I'm worn out with exhaustion and chronic queasiness. I wake in the middle of the night and feel hysteria all around me—not lurking, not ready to pounce, but seeping through the room like gas. I press myself into Mike's flannel-clad back and fight the urge to bite clean through his backbone. I haven't told him yet. I think about abortion but I know I couldn't go through with it—even if I could find someone who wasn't a butcher, even if I started hanging around poolrooms and downtown bars to find out a name, a referral, even if I told Mike I wanted a week's vacation in Puerto Rico by myself and he agreed to stay home with the children ha ha ha ha ha. . . . But I couldn't. The idea is too grisly. Not the idea, the reality. To rip out a life like that, to rip it out of me and rinse it down some stainless-steel drain. But suppose I were desperate enough, would I do it? Probably. I guess that's my biggest problem. I despair, but I'm not desperate. In frustration I watch my own life go down the drain but I know I can cope with that. I'll survive. I'm strong, and even now, feeling sick all the time, I get goose-pimply with the anticipation of birth. I labor easily, though under delusion. I'm a lucky woman.

Goddamn him. I'll get a full-time housekeeper out of this one. I'll fix him. Let him see if he has any extra fifteen hundred dollars from now on to keep the niggers out of the neighborhood. Or to contribute to this or that one's campaign. Or to entertain on. I'll put laxatives in the pâté and Spanish Fly in the roe. Oh he's so cool, he has everything so neatly under control. He won't even divorce me, he says children need a mother, and then he keeps giving me more children to prove it. Irrefutable logic. He and Father Zimmel, incestuous twins! Why won't rhythm work for me? I've licked the glass off half a dozen thermometers—I should have swallowed the mercury—and each time I have either a boy or a girl for my bother. Suppose I called in the carpenters and had an extra wing built onto the house. Put up a sign: No Admittance Except With Prophylactic In Hand. But he'd see me locked away in a home for the unfit, he'd have me committed to an institution before he'd walk in that door.

And me? I? What options do I have? I'm that sexually sloppy Jewess his mother warned him about. "Jews are sexually sloppy," she told him, and she pursed her lips in scorn and fear; an Irish parody of a Jewish mother. And what of it, I gloried at the time, I'm rich with the juices of honey and pressed olives. Or was . . . But that's *it*, that's what I have to guard against. Not the frustration, not even the encroaching hysteria, but the wine turning to vinegar. The slow corrosion, the final bankruptcy. Of all defeats that's the most insidious. Its tentacles are silent, it sidles up and grabs you over coffee, and you're caught. Bitterness and anger—you can hear your own death rattles.

He won't divorce me, that's sure as the night, the day. Just let me even see a lawyer, he said, and I'd rue the day forever. The children would be caught like butterflies in a net; he'd see to it that he was left with the net. The depth and breadth of his arrogance never stop surprising me. I live in the wrong century. In another time I could have hired a band of thugs to waylay him on a dark night and do their swift razor work. Poor denuded Abelard, singing mournfully to himself, No no, they can't take that away from me. Mike impotent, the loveliest of lovers. I won't hire anyone, I'll do the dire deed myself, and I won't use a razor, not even a rusty one; I'll use the goddamned pruning shears.

Maybe when I tell Mike he'll give me another diamond sunburst. Diamonds are a girl's best friend—I'll pin it between my legs. Won't he be surprised! He thinks I care about the jewelry, the furs, he honestly thinks they should make a woman happy. I could be happy in Ludeyville with Moses Herzog, that's how I could be happy. Well, it's no use. My sagging breasts wouldn't please him, neither would my reluctance to nourish his ego. My own inner house needs refurbishing; I couldn't take on the care and feeding of his. Let that fantasy go. I'll survive this baby, I'll name it Omega—just the way I named the last five. Those Greeks, they just didn't know where to end their alphabet. Should I have an abortion or a frontal lobotomy. I'm being funny again, I can't even despair properly. The odd thing is, I don't feel suicidal. I feel used, angry, vindictive—and this *will* be the last baby, I swear that—but not suicidal. Please God in my next rein-carnation I'll come back as other than a cow or a dancing bear. A fish, a Clown Loach—that would suit me. An electric stargazer: I shoot out my tongue to trap my victims and emit fifty-volt charges. (Though that sounds more like Mike.) I'll be a Moray eel, ferocious; powerful jaws, strong teeth, a savage bite. I'll be a Porcupine Globefish, inflating myself when in danger, with erected spines—why hasn't anyone thought of that before as a birth-control measure? A Brown-headed Cowbird who lays her eggs in other birds' nests; nasty wily lady, she then takes off and someone else has to brood and rear her young. I'd like to be a wild horse, even a deer—but then there's hunting season and I don't want any strain on me, any tension. Not the next time around.

Once in the Baltimore zoo I saw a guanaco. Standing so close to the fence that I could have reached in and touched her eyelashes, still she didn't move and neither did I. Her eyes were extraordinarily beautiful. Deep brown, lambent. Lashes a full inch long, thick as a painter's brush. Straight. Her fur a rich red brown, whitish underneath; black forehead and head patches. For all I know guanacos are as stupid as mules, but I know this one was not. She stood poised in perfection and it didn't matter that she was behind a Baltimore fence and not roaming the Patagonian uplands and valleys. I wanted to climb inside her skin and look out at me on the other side of the fence. I ached to reach in and stroke her, but for the world I wouldn't have demeaned her with a pat. When a kid came by and threw a handful of popcorn at her she didn't move a foreleg. Not even a glance. Keep your lousy popcorn, we guanacos are an ancient race. We may not fly, or arrow through the oceans, we may not terrorize the jungle, but we copulate with gusto, we rear our young with affection, and then free them to early independence, we're agile, curious, gentle, loyal. We have our own vision. So take your popcorn and stuff it.

She wouldn't have said that: take your popcorn and stuff it. She wasn't vulgar. But I must stop this. I'm way behind on mending, on reading. I'll come back to you, guanaco, another time.

My Neighbor

Gary Gildner

is showing my daughter
his new can of Mace
his double locks
his baseball bat
his chunky face
all smiles when
our dogs romp over
"jaws" he whispers
"damage" "throat"
and swooning pats
her little head.

Prayer

Gary Gildner

OUR Father we want to be happy
We want the easy instructions easy
We want You to be sensible and our children rich
We ourselves want to be sensible and rich
We don't want the poor to be poor
We want them to roll their eyes forward

And we want the animals to smile when we snap their
    picture
And we don't want to hear that the forests are closing up
And we don't want to hear that the water has sores
And we don't want to hear that the air is crawling

We take our dogs to the doctor
And we wash and rinse and hit the line

World without end. Amen.

(Continued from page 10)
Eastern religions. This is an extension of some of the underlying assumptions of Vatican II in 1962. Vatican II, the "Ecumenical" Council, was not, in fact, very ecumenical: it was a Latin show, called and run by the Latin Church. Included were some of the Patriarchs of the Eastern-rite Churches, their flowing beards and long black robes contrasting with the scarlet and purple silks of the clean-shaven Westerners. Protestant and Orthodox Christians attended only as observers, as did Jews and other nonbelievers. The few Roman Catholic women who attended or addressed the hierarchy were there merely as observers, and were turned away from the communion rail. Basically it was the old closed shop of the cardinals and the prelates with their *periti,* scholar-advisers, at their elbows.

The cardinals of the Curia, the overwhelmingly Italian working administration of the Church, played an obstructionist role, and were generally thought to be bent on sabotaging the Council's intentions, which were, as John had said simply, "to open the windows," and to start the process of *aggiornamento,* literally "to bring up to today." The Dutch Belgian-German coalition on the liberal side, with scattered support from France, Latin America, and Africa, argued for the Twentieth Century against most of the Italians, Spaniards, Irish and Americans who supported an array of other centuries and cultures, mostly representing the Thirteenth, the Renaissance, the Counter-Reformation, and the Vatican and home-town City Hall. The Pope, John and then Paul VI, was present only on ceremonial occasions, and watched the proceedings from the protection of his apartment. The liberals were energetic lobbyists, and the rightists of the Curia stooped to criminal methods when outvoted or outshouted.

Out of all this, some documents were produced and voted on, the most famous of which absolved the Jews of deicide. On balance, the liberals were thought to have won, if ever so slightly. Documents were promulgated on social justice, and on the responsibility of rich nations toward poor ones. The mood was "relevance." The bishops were encouraged to think of themselves as sharing with the

Pope the responsibility for the Church's *magesteriam*, but in fact the Council did not move, and the Vatican still has not moved, on the administrative reforms that could loosen the centrist Roman grasp.

The liturgy, and most particularly the Mass, the central Christian celebration, was updated, its forms shortened, and the use of the vernacular was mandated. Latin was no longer to be the "sacred" language of the Church. It was hard to entertain arguments as to its practicality as a tool of a "universal" Church, since the multilingual translation facilities that had been installed for the observers were the envy of the bishops, many of whom openly admitted they could not understand the long Latin discourses.

What next? For this is where Moore's story takes us. If not too much flew in the windows of the Vatican in real reform and substantive change, the Council did have a tremendous effect on those among us who had been schooled in the "Old Church," the Church of the Abbot of Moore's tale and of Anne Higgins' troubled protagonist. Its critics called this metamorphosis anarchy, but for some in the community it was a freeing from the debilitating strain of public conformity and private doubt that lays such a burden on the woman in the Higgins story. It was an opportunity to look publicly at doubt and, as a community, at faith. For some it was also a freeing from the kind of humiliating act that this woman is forced into when she goes off secretly to get her IUD, and the chance to leave ourselves and each other room enough to make a recommitment that might be a loving act.

As Moore imagines it, there has been another Council, possibly in the mid-1970s and yet another in the mid-1980s. Rome has conceded much of its former authority to a central Ecumen, and the Church, in a vastly modified form, has hung together instead of splitting off into a variety of schisms. So now it is not Rome alone, but Rome in conjunction with the Ecumen in Amsterdam, which sends its bureaucrat hustling up to Ireland to put down the mini-revolt. There it is all over again, the old Triumphalism.

The embattled Abbot believes that faith is a gift of God, and that prayer is the "only miracle." When he was a young man, the changes in the Church dating from Vatican II had set him doubting, and because of those fearful doubts, he has from that time frequently been unable to pray. He exists in a state of what he thinks of as "null and void," in the dark night of the soul the mystics John of the Cross and Teresa of Avila spoke of. The Latin Mass his monastery celebrates is seen by the authorities as an act of disobedience and defiance, a source of potential embarrassment to them on the eve of negotiations with the Buddhists. But for him, it is a way to try to pray, to serve as minister to the pilgrims who come to hear it, and as an expression of his duty not to disturb the faith of his communicants. The Abbot, at least, knows that faith is mysterious, and he knows that it is easily disturbed, since he has suffered himself that agony. "I don't know what God's truth is. Do any of us?" he asks.

Whereas the project-analyst from Rome, the young priest Kinsella, seems never to have been touched by doubt, and gives no indication that he puts faith in the center of the religious act. Kinsella is a new Triumphalist, condescending to the old monks with their primitive ideas of what the Mass is, and who Christ is, and concerned only with achieving the politically necessary "uniform posture." The Church *will* prevail, this time as revolution, which is the "established faith and will prevail."

The young Kinsella is all modernity on the outside, in dress, speech, and dogma, but deep down he conforms to the old rules of orthodoxy and discipline. The Abbot, with his old-fashioned cassock, Latin, and private confession, is much more an existential Christian in his struggle to understand the realities of faith and of his priestly vocation.

But perhaps old and new are not the only ways to think about the complexities of Moore's story, just as contraception is not the sole difficulty for the woman in Higgins' story. The Abbot and that woman are more than "Catholics"; they have interior lives. Both understand that faith cannot be ordered and that the miracle is between man and God. "If our words become prayer," the Abbot says, "God will come."

While the official Church, in these stories, rides herd over some human beings, others faithfully search their souls for ways of finding salvation. Kinsella acts as if he, and his New Church, have all the answers. And the old monk, like the saints, the mystics, and the modern Christian existentialists such as Mounier and Kierkegaard, searches for God from the hollow of peril and exile.

AM

Contributors

John Barth is the author of *The Sot-Weed Factor, End of the Road,* and *Giles Goat-Boy. Joe David Bellamy* teaches English at Mansfield State College and is at work on a book of interviews with "innovative fiction writers."

Alfred Chester, one of the most gifted writers of the middle generation, died in Jerusalem last year. Mr. Chester was the author of two novels, *Jamie Is My Heart's Desire* and *The Exquisite Corpse,* and a collection of stories, *Behold Goliath.* "The Foot," a novella, was published in *NAR* 9.

B. H. Friedman's books include the novels *Circles* and *Yarborough* and the biography *Jackson Pollock: Energy Made Visible.* Part of another novel, *Whispers,* appeared in *NAR* 5.

Patricia Goedicke lives in Mexico. Her first collection, *Between Oceans,* was issued by Harcourt, Brace in 1968.

Michael Goldman teaches English at Columbia. His books include *First Poems, At the Edge,* and, most recently, *Shakespeare and the Energies of Drama.*

Gary Gildner has contributed poems to *Lillabulero, Sumac,* and other magazines. Two collections, *First Practice* and *Digging for Indians,* were brought out by University of Pittsburgh Press.

Marilyn Hacker's poems have appeared in *Aphra, Arx, ManRoot* and *NAR* 11 and 13 among other periodicals.

Bill Henkin has worked on *TriQuarterly* and *Playboy* and co-edited two anthologies, *Contemporary Latin American Literature* and *Under Thirty*. *Toward Skiles*, a book of poems, was issued by Rain Books in 1970.

Anne Higgins is her own writer-in-residence in Schenectady, New York. She is married, has five children, a dog, cats, gerbils, fish, etc., and contributes fiction to *Red Clay Reader* and other magazines.

Stewart Lindh, an MFA candidate at Columbia, is presently living and writing in New York City.

Al Levine is currently growing the longest beard of any poet on New York's Upper West Side. *Prophecy in Bridgeport and Other Poems* will be published by Scribner's this fall.

James Martin studied theology at Edinburgh University in Scotland last year. "A Reunion," a poem about the Cocoanut Grove fire, appeared in *NAR 12*.

William Mathes has been working on the screenplay of his story "Swan Feast," which was published in *NAR 1*. *Minotaur, Minotaur*, a novel, came out in 1967, and he's currently working on two other novels.

Alice Mattison lives in California. This is her first published poem.

Ian McEwan, a master's candidate at the University of East Anglia, England, lives in Norfolk and has recently traveled through the wastes of Iran. This is his second published story.

W. S. Merwin's most recent books are *Selected Translations, The Miner's Pale Children*, and *The Carrier of Ladders*.

Brian Moore's *The Revolution Script* was issued by Holt last year. Among his novels are *The Lonely Passion of Judith Hearne, The Luck of Ginger Coffey, An Answer from Limbo*, and *The Emperor of Ice-Cream*.

James Reiss teaches English at Miami University in Oxford, Ohio. He has contributed to *Prairie Schooner,* the *New Republic, Poetry Northwest,* and other periodicals.

Muriel Rukeyser's books include *The Speed of Darkness* and *The Traces of Thomas Hariot.* Her poems have appeared in *Antaeus, New York Quarterly, Transatlantic Review,* and other magazines.

Anne Sexton won a Pulitzer Prize for her collection, *Live or Die.* Among her other books are *To Bedlam and Part Way Back, All My Pretty Ones,* and, most recently, *Transformations.*

Gary Snyder is the author of *Riprap, Myths & Texts, Earth House Hold,* and other books.

Gilbert Sorrentino's story "The Moon in Its Flight" appeared in *NAR 13.* A novel, *Imaginative Qualities of Actual Things,* came out last year.

David Young teaches English at Oberlin. *Sweating Out the Winter,* a collection of poems, was issued by University of Pittsburgh Press; he is currently working on translations from the Italian, German, and Chinese.

Complete Your Set of NAR

Issues 1–13 are going out of print. We have a limited supply available at $.75 each.

☐ NAR #1   William H. Gass *In the Heart of the Heart of the Country*, Philip Roth *The Jewish Blues*, William Mathes *Swan Feast*, Stanley Kauffmann *Drama on The Times*, Benjamin DeMott *"But He's a Homo-Sexual . . . ,"* Grace Paley *Faith: In a Tree . . .*

☐ NAR #2   Alan Friedman *Willy-Nilly*, John Barth *Autobiography*, Nat Hentoff *Reflections on Black Power*, Arlene Heyman *Strains of Iris*, Günter Grass *Four Poems . . .*

☐ NAR #3   George Dennison *The First Street School*, Donald Barthelme *Robert Kennedy Saved from Drowning*, Paul West *A Passion to Learn*, Philip Roth *Civilization and Its Discontents*, Albert Goldman *The Emergence of Rock . . .*

☐ NAR #4   Robert Coover *The Cat in the Hat for President*, C. C. O'Brien *Politics as Drama as Politics*, Mordecai Richler *A Sense of the Ridiculous*, Alan Lelchuk *Of Our Time*, Richard Gilman *The True and Only Crisis of the Theatre . . .*

☐ NAR #5   Pat Watters *"Keep on A-Walkin', Children,"* Wilfrid Sheed *Eugene McCarthy*, Eric Bentley *The Unliberated University*, Jay Neugeboren *Reflections at Thirty*, Jules Siegel *The Man Who Believed in Christmas Trees . . .*

☐ NAR #6   Jane Jacobs *Why Cities Stagnate*, Ellen Willis *Lessons of Chicago*, Robert Stone *Porque No*

Tiene . . . , William H. Gass *We Have Not Lived the Right Life*, Eric Salzman *The Revolution in Music . . .*

□ NAR #7   Kate Millett *Sexual Politics*, Rosalyn Drexler *Like . . .* , Michael Herr *Illumination Rounds*, L. Woiwode *Don't You Wish You Were Dead . . .*

□ NAR #8   John H. Schaar *Reflections on Authority*, George Dennison *On Being a Son*, Eric Bentley *Theater and Therapy*, Theodore Solotaroff *Silence, Exile, and Cunning*, Ernest Callenbach *The Death of the Movie Aesthetic . . .*

□ NAR #9   Alfred Chester *The Foot*, Theodore Roszak *The Artificial Environment*, Samuel R. Delany *The Unicorn Tapestry*, Richard Gilman *Jerzy Grotowski*, *Symposium: The Writer's Situation I . . .*

□ NAR #10   Philip Roth *On the Air*, William H. Gass *In Terms of the Toenail: Fiction and the Figures of Life*, Arno Karlen *The Guardian*, Jules Siegel *Family Secrets, Symposium: The Writer's Situation II . . .*

□ NAR #11   M. F. Beal *Gold*, Paul West *The Season of the Single Women*, Michael Rossman *The Day We Named Our Child*, Robert Coover *The Last Quixote*, Nicholas von Hoffman *Nixon*, Norman Martien *Getting Out of Schools, Symposium: The Writer's Situation III . . .*

□ NAR #12   A. Alvarez *Sylvia Plath: A Memoir*, Norman Mailer *A Course in Film-Making*, Robert Coover *Love Scene*, Michael Rossman *Introduction to Dome-Building: A Geodesic Meditation*, Donald Barthelme *Alexandria and Henrietta*, Richard Brautigan *The World War I LA Airplane . . .*

☐ NAR #13   James McCourt *Mawrdew Czgowchwz,* Gabriel García Márquez *A Very Old Man with Enormous Wings,* Jorge Luis Borges *Guayaquil,* Leonard Michaels *Storytellers, Liars, and Bores,* Gilbert Sorrentino *The Moon in Its Flight,* Joyce Carol Oates *Others' Dreams,* Grace Paley *A Conversation with My Father . . .*

☐ NAR #14   Randall Reid *Detritus,* Doris Lessing *An Old Woman and Her Cat,* Reynolds Price *For Ernest Hemingway,* Kenneth Bernard *King Kong: A Meditation,* Robert Coover *Lucky Pierre and the Music Lesson,* Peter Steinfels *The Counterintellectuals . . .*

New American Review
Subscription Dept., Simon & Schuster, Inc.
1 West 39th Street, New York, N.Y. 10018

Please send me the copies of *New American Review* checked above.

Enclosed is my check for $_____, calculated at $.75 per copy.

Name _____

Address _____

City _____ State _____ Zip Code _____

Please allow at least three weeks for delivery.
Foreign orders: add $.50 per copy for postage.